Organic Chemistry Lab Manual CHM 237

Arizona State University

Donald L. Pavia

CENGAGE
Learning™

Australia • Brazil • Japan • Korea • Mexico • Singapore • Spain • United Kingdom • United States

CENGAGE
Learning™

Organic Chemistry Lab Manual CHM 237: Arizona State University
Donald L. Pavia

Executive Editor:
Michael Stranz

Custom Editor:
Name LastName

Marketing Specialist:
Courtney Sheldon

Production Editorial Manager:
Kim Fry

Custom Production Editor:
Name LastName

Senior Production / Manufacturing Manager:
Donna M. Brown

Project Coordinator:
Amy McCormick

Senior Rights Acquisition Account Manager:
Todd Osborne

Cover Designer:
Nick Barrows

Cover Image:
Name LastName (from spreadsheet)

Compositor:
MPS Limited, A Macmillan Company

© 2011 Cengage Learning

For product information and technology assistance, contact us at
Cengage Learning Customer & Sales Support, 1-800-354-9706

For permission to use material from this text or product, submit all requests online at **cengage.com/permissions**
Further permissions questions can be emailed to
permissionrequest@cengage.com

ISBN-13: 978-1-111-77605-3

ISBN-10: 1-111-77605-9

Cengage Learning
5191 Natorp Boulevard
Mason, OH 45040
USA

Cengage Learning is a leading provider of customized learning solutions with office locations around the globe, including Singapore, the United Kingdom, Australia, Mexico, Brazil, and Japan. Locate your local office at:
international.cengage.com/region

Cengage Learning products are represented in Canada by Nelson Education, Ltd.

Visit Signature Labs online at **signaturelabs.com**

Visit our corporate website at **cengage.com**

Printed in the United States of America

Acknowledgements

The content of this text has been adapted from the following product(s):

Experiment 3: Crystallization – Microscale – Pavia
ISBN 10: (0-495-30309-7)
ISBN 13: (978-0-495-30309-1)

Experiment 4: Extraction – Microscale – Pavia
ISBN 10: (0-495-30310-0)
ISBN 13: (978-0-495-30310-7

Experiment 7: Infared Spectroscopy and Boiling-Point Determination – Microscale – Pavia
ISBN 10: (0-495-30313-5)
ISBN 13: (978-0-495-30313-8)

Experiment 9: Isolation of the Active Ingredient in an Analgesic Drug – Microscale – Pavia
ISBN 10: (0-495-30318-6)
ISBN 13: (978-0-495-30318-3)

Experiment 10: Acetaminophen – Microscale – Pavia
ISBN 10: (0-495-30319-4)
ISBN 13: (978-0-495-30319-0)

Experiment 11: TLC Analysis of Analgesic Drugs – Microscale – Pavia
ISBN 10: (0-495-30321-6)
ISBN 13: (978-0-495-30321-3)

Experiment 13: Isopentyl Acetate (Banana Oil) – Microscale – Pavia
ISBN 10: (0-495-30325-9)
ISBN 13: (978-0-495-30325-1)

Experiment 20: Reactives of Some Alkyl Halides – Pavia – Pavia
ISBN 10: (0-495-30339-9)
ISBN 13: (978-0-495-3009-8)

Experiment 25: 4-Methylcyclohexene – Microscale – Pavia
ISBN 10: (0-495-30344-5)
ISBN 13: (978-0-495-30344-2)

Table Of Contents

LAB A:
ADAPTED FROM EXPERIMENT #3

Microscale Crystallization—Craig Tube

PROCEDURE

Preparations

Weigh 0.10 g of impure sulfanilamide and transfer this solid to a Craig tube. To a small test tube, add 2–3 mL of 95% ethyl alcohol and a boiling stone. Heat the solvent on a *warm (not hot)* hot plate with an aluminum block until the solvent is boiling.[4] Setting the temperature of the hot plate too high will result in too much loss of solvent through evaporation.

> **CAUTION**
>
> **In performing the following procedure, keep in mind that the mixture in the Craig tube may erupt out of the tube if it becomes superheated. You can prevent this by stirring the mixture constantly with the spatula and by avoiding overheating the mixture.**

Dissolving the Sulfanilamide

Before heating the Craig tube containing the sulfanilamide, add enough hot solvent with a Pasteur pipet to barely cover the crystals. Then heat the Craig tube containing the sulfanilamide until the solvent is boiling. At first, this may be difficult to see because so little solvent is present. Add another small portion of solvent (one or two drops), continue to heat the Craig tube, and stir the mixture by rapidly twirling a microspatula between your fingers. When you have stirred the mixture for 10–15 seconds, check to see whether the solid has dissolved. If it has not, add another portion (one or two drops) of solvent. Heat the Craig tube again with stirring until the solvent boils. Then stir the tube for 10–15 seconds. Continue repeating this process of adding solvent, heating, and stirring until all the solid has dissolved completely. Note that is it essential to add just enough solvent to dissolve the solid—neither too much nor too little. Because 95% ethyl alcohol is very volatile, you need to perform this entire procedure fairly rapidly. Otherwise, you may lose solvent nearly as rapidly as you are adding it, and this procedure will take a very long time. The time from the first addition of solvent until the solid dissolves completely should be no longer than 10–15 minutes.

---

[4] You may also use a hot water bath to heat the solvent in the test tube and to heat the Craig tube. The temperature of the water bath should be about 80°C.

Crystallization

Remove the Craig tube from the heat and insert the inner plug into the opening. Allow the Craig tube to cool slowly to room temperature by placing it into a 10-mL Erlenmeyer flask. Crystallization should begin by the time the Craig tube has cooled to room temperature. If it has not, *gently* scratch the inside surface of the tube with a glass rod (not fire-polished) to induce crystallization.[5] When it appears that no further crystallization is occurring at room temperature, place the Craig tube in an ice-water bath using a beaker. Be sure that both water and ice are present and that the beaker is small enough to prevent the Craig tube from tipping over.

Isolation of Crystals

When crystallization is complete, place the Craig tube in a centrifuge tube and separate the crystals from the mother liquor by centrifugation.

Using the copper wire, pull the Craig tube out of the centrifuge tube. If the crystals collected on the end of the inner plug, remove the plug and scrape the crystals with a spatula onto a preweighed watch glass for air-drying. Otherwise, it will be necessary to scrape the crystals from the inside surface of the outer part of the Craig tube. If you will be doing the Optional Exercise, save the mother liquor in the centrifuge tube. Separate the crystals as much as possible with a spatula. The crystals should be completely dried within 5–10 minutes. You can determine if the crystals are still wet by observing whether or not they stick to a spatula or stay together in a clump. Weigh the dry crystals and calculate the percent recovery. Determine the melting point of both the pure sulfanilamide and the original impure material. At the option of the instructor, turn in your crystallized material in a properly labeled container.

EXPERIMENT 3C

Selecting a Solvent to Crystallize a Substance

In this experiment you will be given an impure sample of fluorene.[6] Your goal will be to find a good solvent for crystallizing the sample. You should try water, methyl alcohol, and toluene. After you have determined which is the best solvent, crystallize the remaining material. Finally, determine the melting point of the purified compound and of the impure sample.

---

[5] An alternative method for inducing crystallization is to dip a microspatula into the solution. Then allow the solvent to evaporate so that a small amount of solid will form on the surface of the spatula. When placed back into the solution, the solid will seed the solution.

[6] The impure fluorene contains 5% fluorenone, a yellow compound.

PROCEDURE

Selecting a Solvent

Perform the procedure given on blackboard with three separate samples of impure fluorene. Use the following solvents: methyl alcohol, water, and toluene.

Crystallizing the Sample

After you have found a good solvent, crystallize the impure fluorene using a semi-microscale (Erlenmeyer flask and Hirsch funnel) or a microscale (Craig tube) procedure. Use 0.3 g of impure fluorene if you follow the semimicroscale procedure, or use 0.05 g if you follow the microscale procedure. Weigh the impure sample carefully, and be sure to keep a little of the impure sample on which to perform a melting point. If you perform a semimicroscale crystallization, you may need to use a size of Erlenmeyer flask different from the one specified in the procedure.

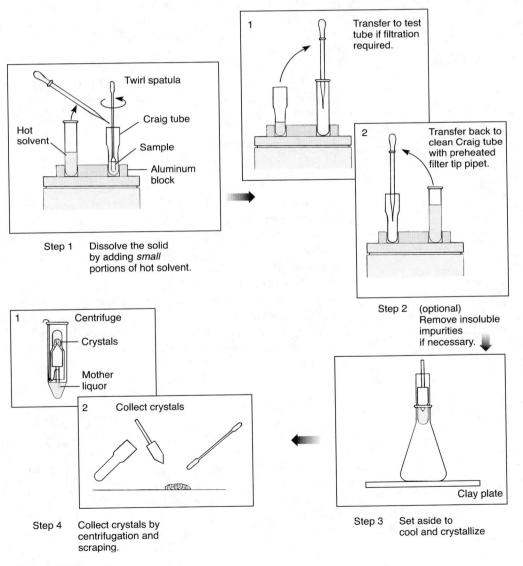

Figure 11.6
Steps in a microscale crystallization (no decolorization).

This decision should be made based on the amount of sample you will be crystallizing and how much solvent you think will be needed. Transfer the crystals to a preweighed watch glass and allow them to air-dry. If water was used as the solvent, you may need to let the crystals sit out overnight for drying because water is less volatile than most organic solvents. Weigh the dried sample and calculate the percent recovery. Determine the melting point of both the pure sample and the original impure material. At the option of the instructor, turn in your crystallized material in a properly labeled container.

EXPERIMENT 3D

Mixture Melting Points

In Experiments 3A and 3B of this experiment, the melting point was used to determine the purity of a known substance. In some situations the melting point can also be used to determine the identity of an unknown substance.

In Experiment 3D, you will be given a pure sample of an unknown from the following list:

Compound	Melting Point (°C)
Acetylsalicylic acid	138–140
Benzoic acid	121–122
Benzoin	135–136
Dibenzoyl ethylene	108–111
Succinimide	122–124
o-Toluic acid	108–110

Your goal is to determine the identity of the unknown using the melting-point technique. If all of the compounds in the list had distinctly different melting points, it would be possible to determine the identity of the unknown by just taking its melting point. However, each of the compounds in this list has a melting point that is close to the melting point of another compound in the list. Therefore, the melting point of the unknown will allow you to narrow down the choices to two compounds. To determine the identity of your compound, you must perform mixture melting points of your unknown and each of the two compounds with similar melting points. A mixture melting point that is depressed and has a wide range indicates that the two compounds in the mixture are different.

PROCEDURE

Obtain an unknown sample and determine its melting point. Determine mixture melting points of your unknown and all compounds from the previous list that have similar melting points. To prepare a sample for a mixture melting point, use a spatula or a glass stirring rod to grind equal amounts of your unknown and the known compound in a watch glass. Record all melting points and state the identity of your unknown.

QUESTIONS

1. Consider a crystallization of sulfanilamide in which 10 mL of hot 95% ethyl alcohol is added to 0.10 g of impure sulfanilamide. After the solid has dissolved, the solution is cooled to room temperature and then placed in an ice-water bath. No crystals form, even after scratching with a glass rod. Explain why this crystallization failed. What would you have to do at this point to make the crystallization work? (You may need to refer to Figure 11.2 below.)

2. Benzyl alcohol (bp 205°C) was selected by a student to crystallize fluorenol (mp 153–154°C) because the solubility characteristics of this solvent are appropriate. However, this solvent is not a good choice. Explain.

3. A student performs a crystallization on an impure sample of biphenyl. The sample weighs 0.5 g and contains about 5% impurity. Based on his knowledge of solubility, the student decides to use benzene as the solvent. After crystallization, the crystals are dried and the final weight is found to be 0.02 g. Assume that all steps in the crystallization are performed correctly, there are no spills, and the student lost very little solid on any glassware or in any of the transfers. Why is the recovery so low?

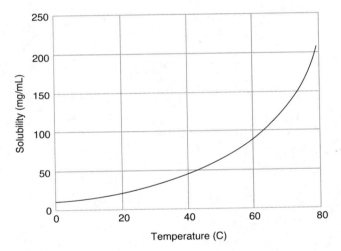

Figure 11.2
Solubility of sulfanilamide in 95% ethyl alcohol.

PostLab: Crystallization & Mixed Melting Point (Exp 3B & 3D)

Note: for all assignment you will not be deducted for poor or missing results *as long as you give valid explanations.*

Group members________________ & ________________

TA ________________________________

Lab Day & Time ________________________________

Grading to be completed by TA	
Experimental Data:	____*/18 pts*
Questions:	____*/12 pts*
Worksheet Total:	____***/30 pts***

Experimental Data and Conclusions (18 points)

Crystallization, Experiment #3B: 10 pts

1. Complete the chart below: (2 pts)

Compound:	Literature Sulfanilamide	Impure Sulfanilamide	Crystallized Sulfanilamide
Melting Point:			

a. Comment on the difference between the impure and crystallized sulfanilamide. What does the difference indicate about your ability to perform an effective crystallization? (2 pts)

b. Comment on the difference between the literature and crystallized sulfanilamide. What does the difference indicate about your product's purity? (2 pts)

2. What was your experimental percent recovery for sulfanilamide in Exp #3B? Show all calculations. (4 points)

Melting Point, Experiment #3D: 8 pts

3. Complete the chart below related to Exp #3D (3 points)

Unknown Code	
Melting point of unknown	
Two possible identities after initial melting point	
Mixed melting point range when mixed with _____ (fill in the blank)	
Mixed melting point range when mixed with _____ (fill in the blank)	
Proposed identity of unknown	

4. Briefly explain the mixed melting point procedure and why it works. Make sure to include a reference to both the range and magnitude of the expected melting points for all aspects of the procedure. (5 points)

Application Questions (12 points)

1. Below are four pairs of similar organic molecules. Circle the molecule in each pair which has the highest boiling or melting point. Provide a brief reason. 4 pts

A) b. pt.

B) b. pt.

C) b. pt.

D) m. pt.

2. Use the graph below to answer the following questions. (8 points total)

Temperature °C	Solubility of A in 100 mL water grams
0	1
20	2
40	5
60	10
80	18

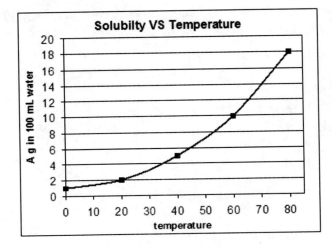

Solubilty VS Temperature

A. What temperature is required to dissolve 4 g of compound A in 100 mL of water? (1 pt)

B. How much compound A will dissolve in 100 mL of water at 70°C? (1 pt)

C. Suppose 8 g of A and 100 mL of water were mixed and heated to 80 °C. The solution was then slowly cooled. At what temperature would crystals of A start to appear? (1 pt)

D. The solution in part C was slowly cooled to 0 °C and the resulting crystals were filtered. What is the expected mass of the collected crystals? (1 pt)

E. What is the percent recovery of the recrystallization performed in parts C and D? (1pt)

F. Suppose 16 g of A and 100 mL of water were mixed and heated to 80 °C. The solution was then cooled slowly to 0 °C. While a lot of product was collected, it was not pure. What was the problem with the procedure that resulted in impure product? (1 pt)

G. Supply at least two things that could be changed in the crystallization procedure to fix the issue in part F so that a pure compound could be obtained. (2 pts)

LAB B:
ADAPTED FROM EXPERIMENT #4

Extraction

Extraction

Critical thinking application

Extraction is one of the most important techniques for isolating and purifying organic substances. In this method, a solution is mixed thoroughly with a second solvent that is **immiscible** with the first solvent. (Remember that immiscible liquids do not mix; they form two phases, or layers.) The solute is extracted from one solvent into the other because it is more soluble in the second solvent than in the first.

Extraction is not only a technique used by organic chemists but it is also used to produce common products with which you are familiar. For example, vanilla extract, the popular flavoring agent, was originally extracted from vanilla beans using alcohol as the organic solvent. Decaffeinated coffee is made from coffee beans that have been decaffeinated by an extraction technique This process is similar to the procedure in Experiment 4A of this experiment, in which you will extract caffeine from an aqueous solution.

The purpose of this experiment is to introduce the microscale technique for performing extractions and allow you to practice this technique. This experiment also demonstrates how extraction is used in organic experiments.

SPECIAL INSTRUCTIONS

Be careful when handling methylene chloride. It is a toxic solvent, and you should not breathe its fumes excessively or spill it on yourself.

In Experiment 4B, it is advisable to pool the data for the distribution coefficients and calculate class averages. This will compensate for differences in the values due to experimental error.

SUGGESTED WASTE DISPOSAL

You must dispose of all methylene chloride in a waste container marked for the disposal of halogenated organic wastes. Place all other organic wastes into the nonhalogenated organic waste container. The aqueous solutions obtained after the extraction steps must be disposed of in the container designated for aqueous waste.

EXPERIMENT 4A

Extraction of Caffeine

One of the most common extraction procedures involves using an organic solvent (nonpolar or slightly polar) to extract an organic compound from an aqueous solution. Because water is highly polar, the mixture will separate into two layers, or phases: an aqueous layer and an organic (nonpolar) layer.

In this experiment, you will extract caffeine from an aqueous solution using methylene chloride. You will perform the extraction step three times using three separate portions of methylene chloride. Because methylene chloride is more dense than water, the organic layer (methylene chloride) will be on the bottom. After each extraction, you will remove the organic layer. The organic layers from all three extractions will be combined and dried over anhydrous sodium sulfate. After transferring the dried solution to a preweighed container, you will evaporate the methylene chloride and determine the weight of caffeine extracted from the aqueous solution. This extraction procedure succeeds because caffeine is much more soluble in methylene chloride than in water.

Pre-Lab Calculation

In this experiment, 0.070 g of caffeine is dissolved in 4.0 mL of water. The caffeine is extracted from the aqueous solution three times with 2.0-mL portions of methylene chloride. Calculate the total amount of caffeine that can be extracted into the three portions of methylene chloride. Caffeine has a distribution coefficient of 4.6, between methylene chloride and water.

PROCEDURE

Preparation

Before beginning this experiment, check your screw-cap centrifuge tube for leaks.[1] Add exactly 0.070 g of caffeine to the centrifuge tube. Then add 4.0 mL of water to the tube. Cap the tube and shake it vigorously for several minutes until the caffeine dissolves completely. It may be necessary to heat the mixture slightly to dissolve all the caffeine.

---

[1] Place about 2 mL of water in the tube. Cap it and shake vigorously. It if leaks, try screwing the cap on more tightly or use a different cap. Sometimes you may need to replace the centrifuge tube itself. Discard the water in the tube.

Extraction

Add 2.0 mL of methylene chloride to the tube. The two layers must be mixed thoroughly so that as much caffeine as possible is transferred from the aqueous layer to the methylene chloride layer. However, if the mixture is mixed too vigorously, it may form an emulsion. Emulsions look like a third frothy layer between the other two layers, and they can make it difficult for the layers to separate. The best way to prevent an emulsion is to shake gently at first and observe whether the layers separate. If they separate quickly, continue to shake, but now more vigorously. The correct way to shake is to invert the tube and right it in a rocking motion. A good rate of shaking is about one rock per second. When it is clear that an emulsion is not forming, you may shake it more vigorously, perhaps two to three times per second. (Note that it is usually not prudent to shake the heck out of it!) Shake the tube for about one minute.

After shaking, place the tube in a test tube rack or beaker and let it stand until the layers separate completely.[2] It may be necessary to tap the sides of the tube to force all the methylene chloride layer to the bottom of the vial. Occasionally, a drop of water will get stuck in the very bottom part of the tube, below the methylene chloride layer. If this happens, depress the bulb slightly and try to draw the water drop into a Pasteur pipet. Transfer this drop to the upper layer.

Using a Pasteur pipet, you should now transfer the organic (bottom) layer into a test tube. Ideally, the goal is to remove all the organic layer without transferring any of the aqueous layer. However, this is difficult to do. Try to squeeze the bulb so that when it is released completely, you will draw up the amount of liquid that you desire. If you have to hold the bulb in a partially depressed position while making a transfer, it is likely that you will spill some liquid. It is also best to transfer the liquid in two steps. First, depress the bulb so that most (about 75%) of the bottom layer will be drawn into the pipet. Place the tip of the pipet squarely in the *V* at the bottom of the centrifuge tube and release the bulb slowly. When making the transfer, it is essential that the centrifuge tube and the test tube be held next to each other. After transferring the first portion, depress the bulb partially, just enough to draw up the remaining liquid in the bottom layer, and place the tip of the pipet in the bottom of the tube. Draw the liquid into the pipet and transfer this liquid to the test tube.

Repeat this extraction two more times using 2 mL of fresh methylene chloride each time. Combine the organic layer from each of these extractions with the methylene chloride solution from the first extraction.

Drying the Organic Layers

Dry the combined organic layers over granular anhydrous sodium sulfate.

Evaporation of Solvent

Transfer the dried methylene chloride solution with a clean, dry Pasteur pipet to a dry, preweighed 10-mL Erlenmeyer flask or test tube while leaving the drying agent behind.[3] (If you had to add more than 3–4 microspatulafuls of anhydrous sodium

---

[2] If an emulsion has formed, the two layers may not separate on standing. If they do not separate after about 1–2 minutes, it will be necessary to centrifuge the mixture to break the emulsion. Remember to balance the centrifuge by placing a tube of equal weight on the opposite side.

sulfate, rinse the sodium sulfate with about 0.5 mL of fresh methylene chloride. Stir this with a dry spatula and then transfer this solution to the same preweighed flask.) Evaporate the methylene chloride by heating the flask in a hot water bath at about 45°C. This should be done in a hood and can be accomplished more rapidly if a stream of dry air or nitrogen gas is directed at the surface of the liquid When the solvent is evaporated, remove the flask from the bath and dry the outside of the flask. When the flask has cooled to room temperature, weigh it to determine the amount of caffeine that was in the methylene chloride solution. Compare this weight with the amount of caffeine calculated in the Pre-Lab Calculation.

EXPERIMENT 4D

Use of Extraction to Isolate a Neutral Compound from a Mixture Containing an Acid or Base Impurity

PROCEDURE

Isolating a Neutral Compound from a Mixture Containing an Acid Impurity. Add 0.150 g of an unknown mixture[5] to a screw-cap centrifuge tube. Add 4.0 mL of ether to the tube and cap it. Shake the tube until all the solid dissolves completely.

Add 2.0 mL of 1.0 M NaOH to the tube and shake for 30 seconds. Let the layers separate. Remove the bottom (aqueous) layer, and place this in a test tube labeled "1st NaOH extract." Add another 2.0-mL portion of 1.0 M NaOH to the centrifuge tube and shake for 30 seconds. When the layers have separated, remove the aqueous layer and put this in a test tube labeled "2nd NaOH extract."

With stirring, add 6 M HCl dropwise to each of the two test tubes containing the NaOH extracts until the mixture is acidic. Test the mixture with litmus or pH paper to determine when it is acidic. Observe the amount of precipitate that forms. What is the precipitate? Does the amount of precipitate in each tube indicate that all the acid impurity has been removed from the ether layer containing the unknown neutral compound?

The drying procedure for an ether layer requires the following additional step compared to the procedure for drying a methylene chloride layer. To the ether layer in the centrifuge tube, add 2.0 mL of saturated aqueous sodium chloride. Shake for 30 seconds and let the layers separate. Remove and discard the aqueous layer. With a clean, dry Pasteur pipet, transfer the ether layer (without any water) to a clean, dry test tube. Now dry the ether layer over granular anhydrous sodium sulfate.

Transfer the dried ether solution with a clean, dry Pasteur pipet to a dry, preweighed test tube, leaving the drying agent behind. Evaporate the ether by heating the tube in a hot water bath. This should be done in a hood and can be accomplished more rapidly if a stream of dry air or nitrogen gas is directed at the

---

[3] It is easier to avoid transferring any drying agent if you use a filter-tip pipet

[5] The mixture contains 0.100 g of one of the neutral compounds given in the list on page 39 and 0.050 g of benzoic acid, the acid impurity.

surface of the liquid. When the solvent has evaporated, remove the test tube from the bath and dry the outside of the tube. Once the tube has cooled to room temperature, weigh it to determine the amount of solid solute that was in the ether layer. Obtain the melting point of the solid and identify it from the following list:

	Melting Point
Fluorenone	82–85°C
Fluorene	116–117°C
1,2,4,5-Tetrachlorobenzene	139–142°C
Triphenylmethanol	162–164°C

Optional Exercise: Isolating a Neutral Compound from a Mixture Containing a Base Impurity. Obtain 0.150 g of an unknown mixture containing a neutral compound and a base impurity.[6] Develop a procedure for isolating the neutral compound, using the preceding procedure as a model. After isolating the neutral compound, obtain the melting point and identify it from the list of compounds given above.

Group member #1 ______________________
Group member #2 ______________________
TA ______________________
Lab Day & Time ______________________

Grading Section to be completed by TA:		
Part I	____	/ 10 pts
Part I	____	/ 12 pts
Part III	____	/ 8 pts
Total	____	***/ 30 pts***

Part I: ***Exp #4A*** ***(10 points)***

1. In this experiment, 0.070 g of caffeine is dissolved in 4.0 mL of water. The caffeine is extracted for the aqueous solution three times with 2.0 mL portions of methylene chloride. The methylene chloride extracts are combined and the solvent evaporated resulting in isolated caffeine crystals. Briefly explain why caffeine will prefer the methylene chloride solvent to the water solvent. To obtain full credit you will need to draw the structures for all three compounds. (2 pts)

2. Calculate the total amount of caffeine that can be extracted in to the three portions of methylene. Caffeine has a distribution coefficient of 4.6, between methylene chloride and water. (4 points)

3. Report the actual amount of caffeine isolated. ____________mg (1pt)

   Compare this weight with the amount of caffeine calculated in the above calculation to determine a percent recovery (isolated/expected x 100%). __________%(1 pt)

   Comment on these values. What do they indicate about your ability to perform an extraction? What could you have done to improve your procedure? (2 points)

1. In this experiment, 0.150 g of a mixture, containing 0.100 g of a neutral unknown compound and 0.050 g of a benzoic acid impurity, is dissolved in 4.0 mL ether. The mixture is extracted two times with 2.0 mL of NaOH ultimately separating the neutral compound and the benzoic acid.

    a. Which compound remains in the ether? _____ (1/2 pt)

    b. Which compound moves to the aqueous NaOH? _____ (1/2 pt)

    c. Provide the chemical reaction that occurred when NaOH was added. Show all lone pair electrons and formal charges. Clearly indicate the difference between an ionic bond and a covalent bond. (2 pts)

2. Following the extraction 6 M HCl was added to both of the NaOH extracts, resulting in a precipitate.
    a. Provide the chemical reaction that occurred when HCl was added. For this reactions use hydronium in place of HCl as that is the active acid. Show all lone pair electrons and formal charges. (2 pts)

    b. What does the amount of precipitate in each tube indicate about the extraction procedure? (1 pt)

3. Following extraction, the ether layer was washed with 2.0 mL saturated aqueous sodium chloride. Briefly explain the purpose of this step. (1 pt)

4. Following the sat. NaCl wash, a small amount of anhydrous sodium sulfate was added to the ether. Briefly explain the purpose of this step. (1 pt)

5. Prior to evaporating the ether in a water bath, the anhydrous sodium sulfate was removed from the ether solution. Briefly explain why the sodium sulfate needed to be removed at this point and not later. (1 pt)

6. What was the melting point range of the compound isolated via extraction in Exp # 4D? _____ (1 pt)

7. What is the proposed identity of the isolated unknown? _____ Draw its structure. (2 pt)

Part III: *Application Question* (8 pts)

Separate the following four compounds using extraction and isolate them in their neutral (as shown) form. Follow the flow chart in Padias (but draw the compounds instead of using the generic "HA," "B," or "N" notation). Notice that in addition to the strong acid with a pKa of 4, a weak acid with a pKa of 10 has also been added to the mixture.

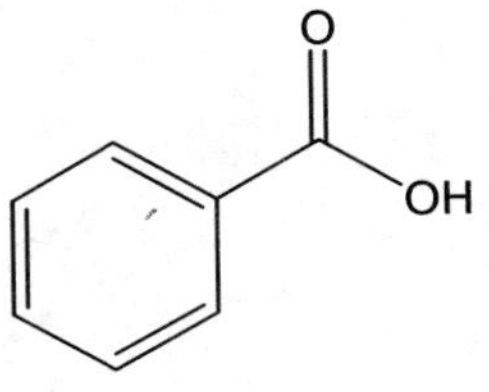

acid
pKa ~ 4

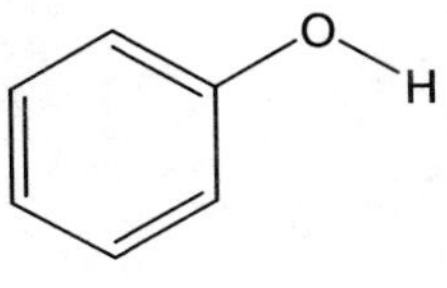

acid
pKa ~ 10

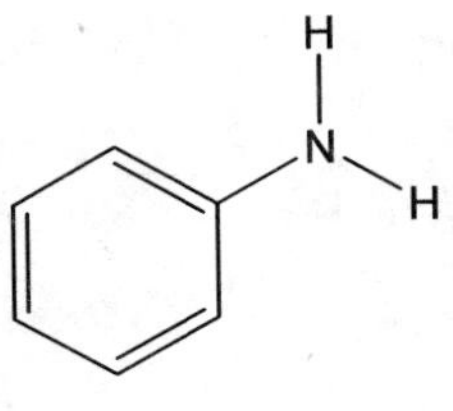

base

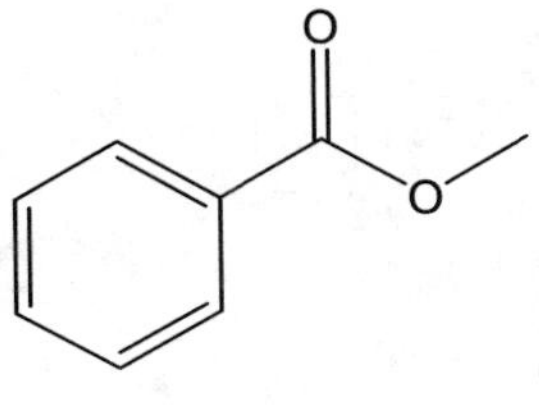

neutral

LAB C:
ADAPTED FROM EXPERIMENT #9

Isolation of the Active Ingredient in an Analgesic Drug

Extraction

Filtration

Melting point

Most analgesic (pain-relieving) drugs found on the shelves of any drug or grocery store generally fall into one of four categories. These drugs may contain **acetylsalicylic acid, acetaminophen,** or **ibuprofen** as the active ingredient, or some **combination** of these compounds may be used in a single preparation. All tablets, regardless of type, contain a large amount of starch or other inert substance. This material acts as a binder to keep the tablet from falling apart and to make it large enough to handle. Some analgesic drugs also contain caffeine or buffering agents. In addition, many tablets are coated to make them easier to swallow and to prevent users from experiencing the unpleasant taste of the drugs.

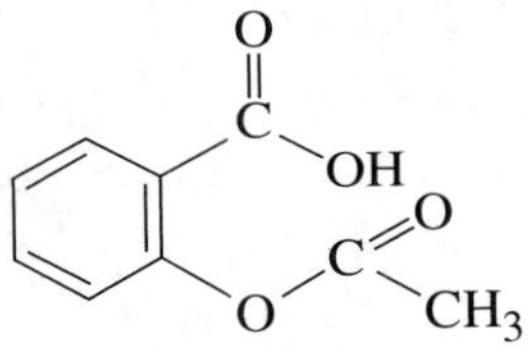

Acetylsalicylic acid

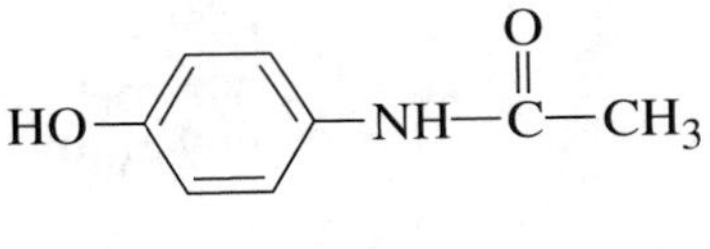

Acetaminophen

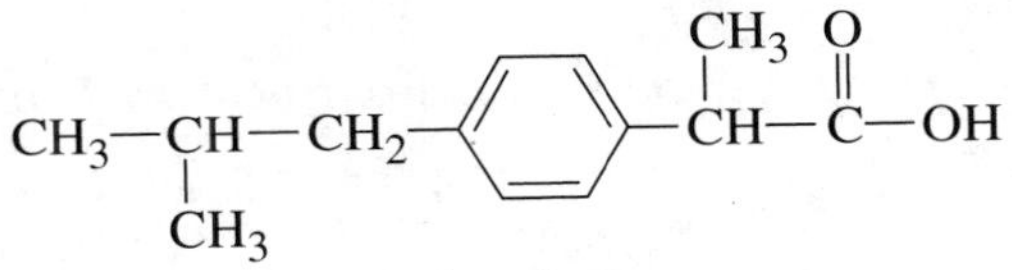

Ibuprofen

The three drugs, along with their melting points (MP) and common brand names, follow:

Drug	MP	Brand Names
Acetylsalicylic acid	135–136°C	Aspirin, ASA, acetylsalicylic acid, generic aspirin, Empirin
Acetaminophen	169–170.5°C	Tylenol, Datril, Panadol, nonaspirin pain reliever (various brands)
Ibuprofen	75–77°C	Advil, Brufen, Motrin, Nuprin

The purpose of this experiment is to demonstrate some important techniques that are applied throughout this textbook and to allow you to become accustomed to working in the laboratory at the microscale level. More specifically, you will extract (dissolve) the active ingredient of an analgesic drug by mixing the powdered tablet with a solvent, methanol. Two steps are required to remove the fine particles of binder, which remain suspended in the solvent. First, you will use centrifugation to remove most of the binder. The second step will be a filtration technique using a Pasteur pipet packed with alumina (finely ground aluminum oxide). The solvent will then be evaporated to yield the solid analgesic, which will be collected by filtration on a Hirsch funnel. Finally, you will test the purity of the drug by doing a melting-point determination.

SPECIAL INSTRUCTIONS

You will be allowed to select an analgesic that is a member of one of the categories described previously. You should use an uncoated tablet that contains only a single ingredient analgesic and binder. If it is necessary to use a coated tablet, try to remove the coating when the tablet is crushed. To avoid decomposition of aspirin, it is essential to minimize the length of time that it remains dissolved in methanol. Do not stop this experiment until after the drug is dried on the Hirsch funnel.

SUGGESTED WASTE DISPOSAL

Dispose of any remaining methanol in the waste container for nonhalogenated organic solvents. Place the alumina in the container designated for wet alumina.

PROCEDURE

Extraction of Active Ingredient

If you are isolating aspirin or acetaminophen, use *one* tablet in this procedure. If you are isolating ibuprofen, use *two* tablets. Using a pestle, crush the tablet (or tablets) between two pieces of weighing paper. If the tablet is coated, try to remove fragments of the coating material with forceps after the tablet is first crushed. Add all the powdered material to a 3-mL conical vial. Using a calibrated Pasteur pipet (p. 11), add about 2 mL of methanol to the vial. Cap the vial and mix thoroughly by shaking. Loosen the cap at least once during the mixing process to release any pressure that may build up in the vial.

Allow the undissolved portion of the powder to settle in the vial. A cloudy suspension may remain even after 5 minutes or more. You should wait only until it is obvious that the larger particles have settled completely. Using a filter-tip pipet transfer the liquid phase to a centrifuge tube. Add a second 2-mL portion of methanol to the conical vial and repeat the shaking process described previously. After the solid has settled, transfer the liquid phase to the centrifuge tube containing the first extract.

Place the tube in a centrifuge along with another centrifuge tube of equal weight on the opposite side. Centrifuge the mixture for two to three minutes. The suspended solids should collect on the bottom of the tube, leaving a clear or nearly clear **supernatant liquid,** the liquid above the solid. If the liquid is still quite cloudy, repeat the centrifugation for a longer period or at a higher speed. Being careful not to disturb the solid at the bottom of the tube, transfer the supernatant liquid with a Pasteur pipet to a test tube or small beaker.

Column Chromatography

Prepare an alumina column using a Pasteur pipet, as shown in the figure. Insert a small ball of cotton into the top of the column. Using a long, thin object such as a glass stirring rod or a wooden applicator stick, push the cotton down so that it fits into the Pasteur pipet where the constriction begins. Add about 0.5 g of alumina to the pipet and tap the column with your finger to pack the alumina. Clamp the pipet in a vertical position so that the liquid can drain from the column into a small beaker or a 5-mL conical vial. Place a small beaker under the column. With a calibrated Pasteur pipet, add about 2 mL of methanol to the column and allow the liquid to drain until the level of the methanol just reaches the top of the alumina. Once methanol has been added to the alumina, the top of the alumina in the column should not be allowed to run dry. If necessary, add more methanol.

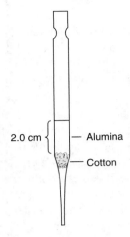

2.0 cm — Alumina

— Cotton

Column for purifying an analgesic drug.

NOTE: It is essential that the methanol not be allowed to drain below the surface of the alumina.

When the level of the methanol reaches the surface of the alumina, transfer the solution containing the drug from the beaker or test tube to the column using a Pasteur pipet. Collect the liquid that passes through the column into a 5-mL conical vial. When all the liquid from the beaker has been added to the column and has penetrated the alumina, add an additional 1 mL of methanol to the column and allow it to drain. This ensures that all the analgesic drug has been eluted from the column.

Evaporation of Solvent

If you are isolating aspirin, it is essential that the following evaporation procedure be completed in 10–15 minutes. Otherwise, the aspirin may partially decompose. Using a Pasteur pipet, transfer about half the liquid in the 5-mL conical vial to another small container. Evaporate the methanol in the 5-mL conical vial using a water bath at about 50°C.[1] To speed evaporation, direct a gentle stream of dry air or nitrogen into the vial containing the liquid. Evaporate the solvent until the volume is less than about 1 mL. Then add the remainder of the liquid and continue evaporation.

When the solvent has completely evaporated or it is apparent that the remaining liquid is no longer evaporating, remove the vial from the water bath (or sand bath) and allow it to cool to room temperature. (The volume of liquid should be less than 0.5 mL when you discontinue evaporation.) If liquid remains, which is likely with the ibuprofen- or acetaminophen-containing analgesics, place the cool vial in an ice-water bath for 10–15 minutes. Prepare the ice-water bath in a small beaker, using both ice and water. Be sure that the vial cannot tip over. Crystallization of the product may occur more readily if you scrape the inside of the vial with a microspatula or a glass rod (not fire-polished). If the solid is hard and clumped, you should use a microspatula to break up the solid as much as possible before going on to the next step.

---

[1] As an alternative, you may use a sand bath at about 50°C.

Vacuum Filtration

Set up a Hirsch funnel for vacuum filtration. Moisten the filter paper with a few drops of methanol and turn on the vacuum (or aspirator) to the fullest extent. Use a microspatula to transfer the material in the conical vial to the Hirsch funnel. The vacuum will draw any remaining solvent from the crystals. Allow the crystals to dry for 5–10 minutes while air is drawn through the crystals in the Hirsch funnel.

Carefully scrape the dried crystals from the filter paper onto a tared (previously weighed) watch glass. If necessary, use a spatula to break up any remaining large pieces of solid. Allow the crystals to air-dry on the watch glass. To determine when the crystals are dry, move them around with a dry spatula. When the crystals no longer clump or cling to the spatula, they should be dry. If you are working with ibuprofen, the solid will be slightly sticky even when it is completely dried. Weigh the watch glass with the crystals to determine the weight of analgesic drug that you have isolated. Use the weight of the active ingredient specified on the label of the container as a basis for calculating the weight percentage recovery.

Use a small sample of the crystals to determine the melting point. Crush the crystals into a powder, using a stirring rod, in order to determine their melting point. You may observe some "sweating" or shrinkage before the substance actually begins to melt. The beginning of the melting-point range is when actual melting is observed, not when the solid takes on a slightly wet or shiny appearance or when shrinkage occurs. If you have isolated ibuprofen, the melting point may be somewhat lower than literature.

At the instructor's option, place your product in a small vial, label it properly (p. 565), and submit it to your instructor.

QUESTIONS

1. Why was the percentage recovery less than 100%? Give several reasons.
2. Why was the tablet crushed?
3. What was the purpose of the centrifugation step?
4. What was the purpose of the alumina column?
5. If 185 mg of acetaminophen were obtained from a tablet containing 350 mg of acetaminophen, what would be the weight percentage recovery?
6. A student who was isolating aspirin stopped the experiment after the filtration step with alumina. One week later, the methanol was evaporated and the experiment was completed. The melting point of the aspirin was found to be 110–115°C. Explain why the melting point was low and why the melting range was so wide.

Postlab: Isolation of an Active Ingredient (Exp9) CHM 237

Name: ______________________________
Name: ______________________________
TA name: ______________________________
Lab Day & Time: ______________________________

Scoring, to be completed by TA
Part I _____ / 10 pts
Part II _____ / 20 pts

TOTAL _____ / 30 pts

Part I: Results (10 pts)

Provide the literature melting points of the three possible active ingredients (1 pt)

Acetylsalicylic acid: ______________
Acetaminophen: ______________
Ibuprofen: ______________

What was the melting point of the active ingredient you isolated? ________________ (2 pt)

What is the most likely identity of the isolated ingredient? ________________ (2 pts)

What was the mass of the active ingredient in the starting tablet (see bottle label): ____________________ (1 pt)

What was the mass of the isolated active ingredient? ________________ (1 pt)

What was the percent recovery: ______________ (1 pt) Show your calculations (2 pts)

Part II: Procdure Questions (20 pts)

Briefly explain the purpose of each step. The steps are listed in the order you will perform them. (2 pts each)

- Crushing the tablet:

- Shaking the crushed tablet in 2 mL methanol:

- Centrifuging the mixture:

- Adding pure methanol to the alumina column:

- Passing the methanol containing the dissolved tablet into the alumina column:

- Evaporation of the methanol solvent:

- Why is it essential to evaporate methanol quickly (within 10-15 minutes) if you are isolating the aspirin?

- Cooling the heated solution (and perhaps placing the cool vial in an ice water bath):

- Filtering the solid:

- Allowing the collected compound to dry before taking a melting point:

- Why is it essential to evaporate methanol quickly (within 10-15 minutes) if you are isolating the aspirin?

LAB D:
ADAPTED FROM EXPERIMENT #7

Infrared Spectroscopy and Boiling-Point Determination

Infrared spectroscopy
Boiling-point determination
Organic nomenclature
Critical thinking application

The ability to identify organic compounds is an important skill that is frequently used in the organic laboratory. Although there are several spectroscopic methods and many chemical and physical tests that can be used for identification, the goal of this experiment is to identify an unknown liquid using infrared spectroscopy and a boiling-point determination. Both methods are introduced in this experiment.

SPECIAL INSTRUCTIONS

Many of the unknown liquids used for this experiment are flammable; therefore, do not use any flames in the laboratory. Also, be careful when handling all of the liquids because many of them are potentially toxic.

This experiment can be performed individually, with each student working on one unknown. However, the opportunity to learn is greater if students work in groups of three. In this case, each group is assigned three unknowns. Each student in the group obtains an infrared spectrum and performs a boiling-point determination on one of the unknowns. Subsequently, the student shares this information with the other two students in the group. Then each student analyzes the collective results for the three unknowns and writes a laboratory report based on all three unknowns. Your instructor will inform you whether you should work alone or in groups.

SUGGESTED WASTE DISPOSAL

If you have not identified the unknown by the end of the laboratory period, you should return the unknown liquid to your instructor in the original container in which it was issued to you. If you have identified the compound, dispose of it in either the container for halogenated waste or the one for nonhalogenated waste, whichever is appropriate.

PROCEDURE

Part A. Infrared Spectrum

Obtain the infrared spectrum of your unknown liquid. If you are working in a group, provide copies of your spectrum for everyone in your group. Identify the significant absorption peaks by labeling them *right on the spectrum,* and include the spectrum in your laboratory report. Absorption peaks corresponding to the following groups should be identified:

C—H (sp^3)

C—H (sp^2)

C—H (aldehyde)

O—H

C=O

C=C (aromatic)

aromatic substitution pattern

C—O

C—X (if applicable)

N—H

Part B. Boiling-Point Determination

Perform a boiling-point determination on your unknown liquid. Your instructor will indicate which method to use. Depending on the method used and the skill of the person performing the technique, boiling points can sometimes be slightly inaccurate. When experimental boiling points are inaccurate, it is more common for them to be lower than the literature value. The difference may be as much as 5°C, especially for higher-boiling liquids. Your instructor may be able to give you more guidance about what level of accuracy you can expect.

Part C. Analysis and Report

Using the structural information from the infrared spectrum and the boiling point of your unknown, identify this liquid from the list of compounds on the next page. If you are working in a group, you will need to do this for all three compounds. In order to make use of the structural information determined from the infrared spectrum, you will need to know the structures of the compounds that have boiling points close to the value you experimentally determined. You may need to consult *The Merck Index* or the *CRC Handbook of Chemistry and Physics.* It may also be helpful to look up these compounds in the index of your lecture textbook. If there is more than one compound that fits the infrared spectrum and is within ±5 degrees of the experimental boiling point, you should list all of these in your laboratory report.

List of possible unknown liquids

Compound	BP (°C)	Compound	BP (°C)
Acetone	56	Butyl acetate	127
2-Methylpentane	62	2-Hexanone	128
sec-Butylamine	63	Morpholine	129
Isobutyraldehyde	64	3-Methyl-1-butanol	130
Methanol	65	Hexanal	130
Isobutylamine	69	Chlorobenzene	132
Hexane	69	2,4-Pentanedione	134
Vinyl acetate	72	Cyclohexylamine	135
1,3,5-Trifluorobenzene	75	Ethylbenzene	136
Butanal	75	p-Xylene	138
Ethyl acetate	77	1-Pentanol	138 —
Butylamine	78	Propionic acid	141
Ethanol	78	Pentyl acetate	142
2-Butanone	80	4-Heptanone	144
Cyclohexane	81	2-Ethyl-1-butanol	146
Isopropyl alcohol	82	N-Methylcyclohexylamine	148
Cyclohexene	83	2,2,2-Trichloroethanol	151
Isopropyl acetate	85	2-Heptanone	151
Triethylamine	89	Heptanal	153
3-Methylbutanal	92	Isobutyric acid	154
3-Methyl-2-butanone	94	Bromobenzene	156
1-Propanol	97	Cyclohexanone	156
Heptane	98	Dibutylamine	159
tert-Butyl acetate	98	Cyclohexanol	160
2,2,4-Trimethylpentane	99	Butyric acid	162
2-Butanol	99	Furfural	162
Formic acid	101	Diisobutyl ketone	168
2-Pentanone	101	Furfuryl alcohol	170
2-Methyl-2-butanol	102	Octanal	171
Pentanal	102	Decane	174
3-Pentanone	102	Isovaleric acid	176
Propyl acetate	102	Limonene	176
Piperidine	106	1-Heptanol	176
2-Methyl-1-propanol	108	Benzaldehyde	179
1-Methylcyclohexene	110	Cycloheptanone	181
Toluene	111	1,4-Diethylbenzene	184
sec-Butyl acetate	111	Iodobenzene	186
Pyridine	115	1-Octanol	195
4-Methyl-2-pentanone	117	Methyl benzoate	199
2-Ethylbutanal	117	Methyl phenyl ketone	202
Methyl 3-methylbutanoate	117	Benzyl alcohol	204
Acetic acid	118	4-Methylbenzaldehyde	204
1-Butanol	118	Ethyl benzoate	212
Octane	126 —		

Names	_____ & _____	
TA	_____	
Lab Day & Time	_____	

To be completed by TA:	
Chart:	____ / 22 pts
IR labels:	____ / 8 pts
Subtotal	____ / 30 pts
TA supplied range	____ / -5 pts
TOTAL	____ / 30

Chart: Complete the chart below regarding your boiling point data, IR data, and conclusions. (22 points)

	Unknown #1	Unknown #2
Unknown code		
Boiling point (required first attempt) **1 point**		NA – because supplied on p. 3 of this handout
Boiling point (required second attempt) **1 point**		NA – because supplied on p. 3 of this handout
If required Boiling point (if needed third attempt)		NA – because supplied on p. 3 of this handout
If you are unable to obtain a reliable b.pt. after 3 attempts, then ask your TA for range. He/she will supply a range, but it will cost you all **5 points from your overall report score.**	Place supplied range here: *TA initials to verify loss of 5 pts:*	NA – because supplied on p. 3 of this handout
Final Experimental Boiling point (or range) **1 point**		Write boiling point range supplied on p. 3 of this handout here:
As a check that your b.pts. are accurate, obtain your TA initial's here. Reports which do NOT contain initials will not be graded. **1 point**	*TA initials to verify accuracy of data:*	NA – because supplied on p. 3 of this handout
Compare your boiling point/range to the chart in Exp 7 Part C. Provide 2 – 10 compounds which **based upon the boiling point alone** could be your unknown. (use ±5 degrees) **2 points**		

Compare your IR to the list of characteristic absorption peaks listed in Exp 7 Part A. List the important peaks in your IR spectrum (these are the functional group peaks, not peaks in the fingerprint region.). Include the units (cm^{-1}), peak shape, and peak intensity. **8 points** Note: These are also the peaks that you need to label on the actual spectrum as described below.		
Based upon your IR, which **functional groups** are present in your unknown? Write their name and draw their basic structure. **4 points**		
Using both the boiling point and the IR data, state the proposed identity (or identities) of your unknown & draw the proposed molecule(s). **4 points**		

IR labeling: Attach the IR spectra of both unknowns to this report. Label each with the following info: (8 points)
- Unknown code
- Name of unknown identity
- Structure of proposed compound
- Match each characteristic functional group peak with specific bond or bond-type in your molecule

Please do not turn this page in.

Unknown Code	BP range
B 1	126 - 135
B 2	126 - 135
B 3	126 - 136
B 4	128 - 138
B 5	126 - 136
B 6	130 - 141
B 7	132 - 142
B 8	132 - 142
B 9	134 - 144
B 10	135 - 146
B 11	138 - 148
B 12	146 - 156
B 13	153 - 162
B 14	154 - 168
B 15	174 - 184
B 16	156 - 168
B 17	159 - 170
B 18	171 - 181
B 19	170 - 181
B 20	162 - 174

LAB E:
ADAPTED FROM EXPERIMENT #10

Acetaminophen

Decolorization

Filtration

Crystallization

Use of a Craig tube or Hirsch funnel

Preparation of an amide

Preparation of acetaminophen involves treating an amine with an acid anhydride to form an amide. In this case, *p*-aminophenol, the amine, is treated with acetic anhydride to form acetaminophen (*p*-acetamidophenol), the amide.

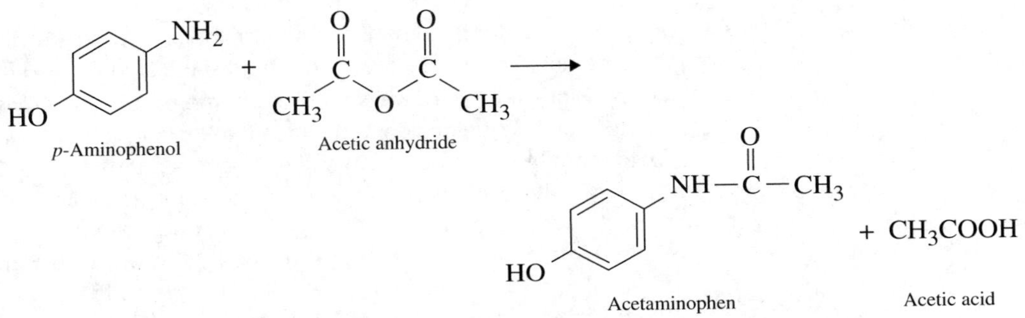

SPECIAL INSTRUCTIONS

Acetic anhydride can cause irritation of tissue, especially in nasal passages. Avoid breathing the vapor, and avoid contact with skin and eyes. *p*-Aminophenol is a skin irritant and is toxic.

WASTE DISPOSAL

Aqueous solutions obtained from filtration operations should be poured into the container designated for aqueous wastes. This includes the filtrates from the methanol and water crystallization steps.

PROCEDURE

Reaction Mixture

Weigh about 0.150 g of *p*-aminophenol (*MW* = 109.1) and place this in a 5-mL conical vial. Using an automatic pipet (or a dispensing pump or a graduated pipet), add 0.450 mL of water and 0.165 mL of acetic anhydride (*MW* = 102.1, *d* = 1.08 g/mL). Place a spin vane in the conical vial and attach an air condenser.

Heating

Heat the reaction mixture with an aluminum block or sand bath at about 120°C and stir gently. If you are using a sand bath, the conical vial should be partially buried in the sand so that the vial is nearly at the bottom of the sand bath. After the solid has dissolved (it may dissolve, precipitate, and redissolve), heat the mixture for an additional 20 minutes to complete the reaction.

Isolation of Crude Acetaminophen

Remove the vial from the heat and allow it to cool. When the vial has cooled to the touch, detach the air condenser and remove the spin vane with clean forceps or a magnet. Rinse the spin vane with two or three drops of warm water, allowing the water to drop into the conical vial. Place the conical vial in a small beaker and let it cool to room temperature. If crystallization has not occurred, scratch the inside of the vial with a glass stirring rod to initiate crystallization. Cool the mixture thoroughly in an ice bath for 15–20 minutes and collect the crystals by vacuum filtration on a Hirsch funnel. Rinse the vial with about 0.5 mL of ice water and transfer this mixture to the Hirsch funnel. Wash the crystals on the funnel with two additional 0.5-mL portions of ice water. Dry the crystals for 5–10 minutes by allowing air to be drawn through them while they remain on the Hirsch funnel. Transfer the product to a watch glass or clay plate and allow the crystals to dry in air. It may take several hours for the crystals to dry completely, but you may go on to the next step before they are totally dry. Weigh the crude product and set aside a small sample for a melting-point determination and a color comparison after the next step. Calculate the percentage yield of crude acetaminophen (*MW* = 151.2). Record the appearance of the crystals in your notebook.

Crystallization of Acetaminophen

Place the purified acetaminophen in a Craig tube. Crystallize the material from a solvent mixture composed of 50% water and 50% methanol by volume (aluminum block or sand bath set at about 100°C). Add small portions (several drops) of hot solvent until the solid dissolves. When the solid has dissolved, place the Craig tube in a 10-mL Erlenmeyer flask, insert the inner plug of the Craig tube, and let the solution cool.

When the mixture has cooled to room temperature, place the Craig tube in an ice-water bath for several minutes. If necessary, induce crystallization by gently scratching the inside of the Craig tube with your microspatula. Because acetaminophen may crystallize *slowly* from the solvent, continue to cool the Craig tube in an ice bath for at least 10 minutes. Collect the crystals. Place the assembly in a centrifuge (be sure it is balanced by a centrifuge tube filled with water so that both tubes contain the same weight) and turn on the centrifuge for several minutes. Collect the crystals on a watch glass or piece of smooth paper. Set the crystals aside to air-dry. Very little additional time should be required to complete the drying.

Yield Calculation and Melting-Point Determination

Weigh the crystallized acetaminophen ($MW = 151.2$) and calculate the percentage yield. This calculation should be based on the number of moles of the limiting reagent used at the beginning of this procedure. Determine the melting point of the product. Compare the melting point of the final product with that of the crude acetaminophen. Also compare the colors of the crude, decolorized, and pure acetaminophen. Pure acetaminophen melts at 169.5–171°C. Place your product in a properly labeled vial and submit it to your instructor.

QUESTIONS

1. During the crystallization of acetaminophen, why was the mixture cooled in an ice bath?

2. In the reaction between *p*-aminophenol and acetic anhydride to form acetaminophen, 0.450 mL of water was added. What was the purpose of the water?

3. Why should you use a minimum amount of water to rinse the conical vial while transferring the purified acetaminophen to the Hirsch funnel?

4. If 0.130 g of *p*-aminophenol is allowed to react with excess acetic anhydride, what is the theoretical yield of acetaminophen in moles? In grams?

5. Give two reasons, discussed in Experiments 8 and 10, why the crude product in most reactions is not pure.

6. Phenacetin has the structure shown. Write an equation for its preparation, starting from 4-ethoxyaniline.

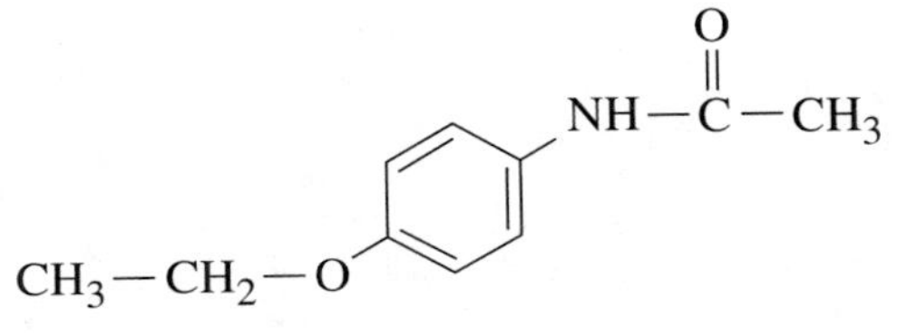

This is a group report worth 50 points.
Groups turning in reports identical or similar to past or current reports will be given an automatic zero.

See the handout called "Report Outline" in the "Course Documents" section for a detailed explanation of report requirements. Figures should be computer generated (there is a link in the external link section on blackboard for free drawing software.)

DIRECTIONS for Typed Report (Be concise! Most typed reports do not need to be more than 5 pages total)
Overall quality (4 points)

Page One
Cover Page (4 points)
Make sure to have an acceptable title. See the outline on blackboard for more detail

Page Two
Abstract (10 points)
A brief summary of the experiment and the results is necessary. Make sure to write out the overall reaction with percent yield. No more than one page double spaced.

Page Three and Following
Introduction (10 points)
The introduction discusses everything you knew and/or expected *prior* to the reaction. It should always include an overall reaction with a verbal explanation.   Once we start learning mechanisms you will also need to include that (so no need to give it for this reaction).   It should also include a description of how you plan to characterize your product (i.e. how will you know if your experiment was successful?) See the handout on blackboard for more detail.
- draw overall reaction using a chemical drawing program
- discuss and explain reaction and reactive species
- discuss expected results/goals
- discuss how you *plan* to characterize product (i.e. mpt and TLC) - but DO NOT give the results yet

Procedure - (5 points)
No more than ½ page double-spaced. Be brief! Use passive past tense and NEVER use I/we.

Results and Calculations (7 points)
This is your "numbers" section. So make sure to supply the literature and experimental melting point of the product. Draw TLC plate, and give TLC Rf values. Supply the percent yield and percent yield calculations.   Tables could be useful here.

Discussion and Conclusions (10 points)
Discuss the overall experiment. The discussion should allude back to everything in the introduction as well as tie-up any unpredicted results. Be sure to discuss all sources of error and possible synthetic routes to improve the reaction and yield.   A good discussion answers the questions "Did it work?", "What good was this?", "Should I change anything next time?" You should explain why it worked, or speculate (based on sound reasoning) why it didn't work. See the handout on blackboard for more detail.

LAB F:
ADAPTED FROM EXPERIMENT #11

TLC Analysis of Analgesic Drugs

THIN-LAYER CHROMATOGRAPHY

In this experiment, thin-layer chromatography (TLC) will be used to determine the composition of various over-the-counter analgesics. If the instructor chooses, you may also be required to identify the components and actual identity (trade name) of an unknown analgesic. You will be given either two or three commercially prepared TLC plates with a flexible backing and a silica gel coating with a fluorescent indicator. On the first TLC plate, a reference plate, you will spot four standard compounds often used in analgesic formulations. In addition, a standard reference mixture containing four of these same compounds will be spotted. On the final plate (the sample plate) you will spot several commercial analgesic preparations in order to determine their composition. At your instructor's option, one or more of these may be an unknown.

The standard compounds will all be available as solutions of 1 g of each dissolved in 20 mL of a 50:50 mixture of methylene chloride and ethanol. The purpose of the first reference plate is to determine the order of elution (R_f values) of the known substances and to index the standard reference mixture. On the second reference plate (optional), several of the substances have similar R_f values, but you will note a different behavior for each spot with the visualization methods. On the sample plate, the standard reference mixture will be spotted, along with several solutions that you will prepare from commercial analgesic tablets. These tablets will each be crushed and dissolved in a 50:50 methylene chloride–ethanol mixture for spotting.

Reference Plate 1		Sample Plate
Acetaminophen	(Ac)	Four commercial
Aspirin	(Asp)	preparations and
Caffeine	(Cf)	unknowns plus
Salicylamide	(Sal)	the reference mixture
Reference mixture 1	(Ref-1)	

Two methods of visualization will be used to observe the positions of the spots on the developed TLC plates. First, the plates will be observed while under illumination from a short-wavelength ultraviolet (UV) lamp. This is best done in a darkened room or in a fume hood that has been darkened by taping butcher paper or aluminum foil over the lowered glass cover. Under these conditions, some of the spots will appear as dark areas on the plate, whereas others will fluoresce brightly. This difference in appearance under UV illumination will help to distinguish the substances from one another. You will find it convenient to outline very lightly in *pencil* the spots observed and to place a small **x** inside those spots that fluoresce. For a second means of visualization, iodine vapor will be used. Not all the spots will become visible when treated with iodine, but some will turn yellow, tan, or deep brown. The differences in the behaviors of the various spots with iodine can be used to further differentiate among them.

It is possible to use several developing solvents for this experiment, but ethyl acetate with 0.5% glacial acetic acid added is preferred. The small amount of glacial acetic acid supplies protons and suppresses ionization of aspirin, ibuprofen, naproxen sodium, and ketoprofen, allowing them to travel upward on the plates in their protonated form. Without the acid, these compounds do not move.

In some analgesics, you may find ingredients besides the five mentioned previously. Some include an antihistamine and some, a mild sedative. For instance, Midol contains N-cinnamylephedrine (cinnamedrine), an antihistamine, and Excedrin PM contains the sedative methapyrilene hydrochloride. Cope contains the related sedative methapyrilene fumarate. Some tablets may be colored with a chemical dye.

SPECIAL INSTRUCTIONS

You must examine the developed plates under ultraviolet light first. After comparisons of *all* plates have been made with UV light, iodine vapor can be used. The iodine permanently affects some of the spots, making it impossible to go back and repeat the UV visualization. Take special care to notice those substances that have similar R_f values; these spots each have a different appearance when viewed under UV illumination or a different staining color with iodine, allowing you to distinguish among them.

Aspirin presents some special problems because it is present in a large amount in many of the analgesics and because it hydrolyzes easily. For these reasons, the aspirin spots often show excessive tailing.

SUGGESTED WASTE DISPOSAL

Dispose of all development solvent in the container for nonhalogenated organic solvents. Dispose of the ethanol–methylene chloride mixture in the container for halogenated organic solvents. The micropipets used for spotting the solution should be placed in a special container labeled for that purpose. The TLC plates should be stapled in your lab notebook.

PROCEDURE

Initial Preparations

You will need at least 12 capillary micropipets (18 if both reference plates are prepared) to spot the plates.

Obtain two (or three) 10-cm × 6.6-cm TLC plates (EM Science Silica Gel 60 F-254, No. 5554-7) from your instructor. These plates have a flexible backing, but they should not be bent excessively. Handle them carefully or the adsorbent may flake off. Also, you should handle them only by the edges; the surface should not be touched. Using a lead pencil (not a pen), *lightly* draw a line across the plates (short dimension) about 1 cm from the bottom. Using a centimeter ruler, move its index about 0.6 cm in from the edge of the plate and lightly mark off six 1-cm intervals on the line (see figure). These are the points at which the samples will be spotted. If you are preparing two reference plates, it would be a good idea to mark a small number **1** or **2** in the upper right-hand corner of each plate to allow easy identification.

Spotting the First Reference Plate

On the first plate (marked 1), starting from left to right, spot acetaminophen, aspirin, caffeine, and salicylamide. This order is alphabetic and will avoid any further memory problems or confusion. The standard reference mixture (Ref-1), The standard reference mixture is spotted in the last position. It is important that the spots be made as small as possible but not too small. With too much sample, the spots will tail and will overlap one another after development. With too little sample, no spots will be observed after development. The optimum applied spot should be about 1–2 mm (1/16 in.) in diameter. If scrap pieces of the TLC plates are available, it would be a good idea to practice spotting on these before preparing the actual sample plates.

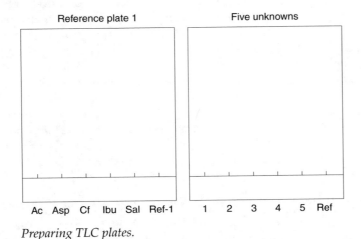

Preparing TLC plates.

Preparing the Development Chamber

When the reference plate has been spotted, obtain a 16-oz wide-mouth, screw-cap jar (or other suitable container) for use as a development chamber. Because the backing on the TLC plates is thin, if they touch the filter paper liner of the development chamber *at any point,* solvent will begin to diffuse onto the absorbent surface at that point.

When the development chamber has been prepared, obtain a small amount of the development solvent (0.5% glacial acetic acid in ethyl acetate). Your instructor should prepare this mixture; it contains such a small amount of acetic acid that small individual portions are difficult to prepare. Fill the chamber with the development solvent to a depth of about 0.5–0.7 cm. Recall that the solvent level must not be above the spots on the plate or the samples will dissolve off the plate into the reservoir instead of developing.

Development of the Reference TLC Plates

Place the spotted plate (or plates) in the chamber (straddling the liner if one is present) and allow the spots to develop. Be sure the plates are placed in the developing jar so that their bottom edge is parallel to the bottom of the jar (straight, not tilted); if not, the solvent front will not advance evenly, increasing the difficulty of making good comparisons. When the solvent has risen to a level about 0.5 cm from the top of the plate, remove plate from the chamber (in the hood) and, using a lead pencil, mark the position of the solvent front. Set the plate on a piece of paper towel to dry. It may be helpful to place a small object under one end to allow optimum air flow around the drying plate.

UV Visualization of the Reference Plates

When the plates are dry, observe them under a short-wavelength UV lamp, prefer-ably in a darkened hood or a darkened room. Lightly outline all of the observed spots with a pencil. Carefully notice any differences in behavior between the spot-ted substances, especially those on plate 2. Several compounds have similar R_f values, but the spots have a different appearance under UV illumination or iodine staining. There are no commercial analgesic preparations containing any com-pounds that have the same R_f values, but you will need to be able to distinguish them from one another to identify which one is present. Before proceeding, make a sketch of the plates in your notebook and note the differences in appearance that you observed. Using a ruler marked in millimeters, measure the distance that each spot has traveled relative to the solvent front. Calculate R_f values for each spot.

Analysis of Commercial Analgesics or Unknowns (Sample Plate)

Next, obtain half a tablet of each of the analgesics to be analyzed on the final TLC plate. Take each analgesic half-tablet, place it on a smoth piece of notebook paper, and crush it well with a spatula. Transfer each crushed half-tablet to a labeled test tube or a small Erlenmeyer flask. Using a graduated cylinder, mix 15 mL of absolute ethanol and 15 mL of methylene chloride. Mix the solution well. Add 5 mL of this solvent to each of the crushed half-tablets and then heat each of them *gently* for a few minutes on a steam bath or sand bath at about 100°C. Not all the tablet will dissolve, because the analgesics usually contain an insoluble binder. In addition, many of them contain inorganic buffering agents or coatings that are insoluble in this solvent mixture. After heating the samples, allow them to settle and then spot the clear liquid extracts on the sample plate. Then spot the unknown mixtures. At the last position, spot the standard reference solution (Ref-1). Develop the plate in 0.5% glacial acetic acid–ethyl acetate as before. Observe the plate under UV illumination and mark the visible spots as you did for the first plate. Sketch the plate in your notebook and record your conclusions about the contents of each tablet and unknown. This can be done by directly comparing your plate to the reference plate(s)—they can all be placed under the UV light at the same time. If you were issued an unknown, try to determine its identity (trade name).

Iodine Analysis

Do not perform this step until UV comparisons of all the plates are complete. When ready, place the plates in a jar containing a few iodine crystals, cap the jar, and warm it gently on a steam bath or warm hot plate until the spots begin to appear. Notice which spots become visible and note their relative colors. You can directly compare colors of the reference spots to those on the unknown plate(s). Remove the plates from the jar and record your observations in your notebook.

QUESTIONS

1. What happens if the spots are made too large when preparing a TLC plate for development?

2. What happens if the spots are made too small when preparing a TLC plate for development?

3. Why must the spots be above the level of the development solvent in the developing chamber?

4. What would happen if the spotting line and positions were marked on the plate with a ballpoint pen?

5. Is it possible to distinguish two spots that have the same R_f value but represent different compounds? Give two different methods.

6. Name some advantages of using acetaminophen (Tylenol) instead of aspirin as an analgesic

Postlab: Thin Layer Chromatography (Exp 11) CHM 237

Names: ____________________
Names: ____________________
TA name: ____________________
Lab Day & Time: ____________________

Scoring, to be completed by TA	
Part I (experiment):	_____ / 15 pts
Part II (questions):	_____ / 15 pts
TOTAL	_____ / 30 pts

Part I: Experiment (15 pts)

Data & Calculations

This section requires you to sketch the chromatographs. The outlines of the TLC plates are shown. When sketching the plates, make sure to:

- draw the starting line (pencil line)
- draw the final position of the solvent front
- mark the final location of the samples/spots
- under the starting line, label the identity of the original spots with the following notations:
  - Ac=acetaminophen
  - Asp = asprin
  - Cf = caffeine
  - Sal = salicylamide
  - Ref = Reference mixture containing Ac, Asp, Cf, & Sal
  - A = Unknown A
  - B = Unknown B
  - C = Unknown C
  - X= Generic tablet X
  - Y = Generic tablet Y (if available)

Sketch the chromatographs as seen under UV light (if you used more than three plates draw in the other plates). (2 points)

Sketch the chromatographs as seen after the I_2 chamber (if you used more than three plates draw in the other plates). (2 points)

Fill in the table provided with the distance traveled by the spot and solvent, as well as the R_f value for each spot. For the commercial drugs there is a heading for spot #1 and #2. For some of the drugs there may only have been one spot. If this is the case then simply write NA in the spaced provided. For a few of the drugs there may be more than 2 spots. If this is the case, then add those in the blanks provided. (6 points)

Identity	Distance Spot traveled	Distance Solvent traveled	R_f Value
Acetaminophen			
Asprin			
Caffeine			
Salicylamide			
Reference spot #1 Identity: _____			
Reference spot #2 Identity: _____			
Reference spot #3 Identity: _____			
Reference spot #3 Identity: _____			
Unknown A spot #1			
Unknown A spot #2 (if present)			
Unknown A spot #3 (if present)			
Unknown B spot #1			
Unknown B spot #2 (if present)			
Unknown B spot #3 (if present)			
Unknown C spot #1			
Unknown C spot #2 (if present)			
Unknown C spot #3 (if present)			
Generic tablet X spot #1			
Generic tablet X spot #2 (if present)			
Generic tablet Y spot #1			
Generic tablet Y spot #2 (if present)			

Experimental Conclusions
For each unknown and tablet which you analyzed, identify each component present in the drug with an "X" in the appropriate box. (5 points)

Drug	Acetaminophen	Asprin	Caffeine	Salicylamide
Unknown A				
Unknown B				
Unknown C				
Generic X				
Generic Y				

Part II: Questions (15 points)

1. What happens if the spots are made too large when preparing a TLC plate for development? (1 pt)

2. What happens if the spots are made too small/dilute when preparing a TLC plate for development? (1 pt)

3. What would a developed TLC plate look like if it was placed in the chamber on a slight angle? (1 pt)

4. What would a developed TLC plate look like if the original plate was placed so that the spotting line was below the developing solvent level? (1 pt)

5. What would a developed TLC plate look like if it the spotting line was drawn in pen instead of pencil? (1 pt)

6. A sample was spotted on two different TLC plates. One plate was placed in a chamber containing methanol, and after developed it showed one spot with an Rf value of 0.97. The other plate was placed in a chamber containing hexane, and after developed it showed **two** spots, one with an Rf value of 0.54 and one with an Rf value of 0.37. Explain how this occurred. (2 pts)

7. A sample was spotted on two different TLC plates. One plate was placed in a chamber containing hexane, and after developed it showed one spot with an Rf value of 0.05. The other plate was placed in a chamber containing ethyl acetate, and after developed it showed **two** spots, one with an Rf value of 0.15 and one with an Rf value of 0.46. Explain how this occurred. (2 pts)

8. You and a classmate were each given a yellow unknown with a melting point of 110°C. You both ran a TLC on it using ethyl acetate solvent as the mobile phase. You both observed a single spot with an Rf value of 0.45. You think you might have the same unknown, but you want to make sure. What TWO relatively quick and easy lab procedures could you do to determine if you have the same unknown? (2 pt)

9. For each set below, rank the molecules according to their polarity (1 = most polar, 3 = least polar) (1 pt)

A.

B.

C.

10. For each set below, rank the molecules according to their TLC Rf values (1 = smallest Rf, 3 = largest Rf) (3 pts)

A.

B.

C.

LAB G:
ADAPTED FROM EXPERIMENT #13

Isopentyl Acetate (Banana Oil)

Esterification

Heating under reflux

Extraction

Simple distillation

Microscale boiling point

In this experiment you will prepare an ester, isopentyl acetate. This ester is often referred to as banana oil because it has the familiar odor of this fruit.

$$CH_3-\overset{\overset{\displaystyle O}{\|}}{C}-OH \ + \ CH_3-\overset{\overset{\displaystyle CH_3}{|}}{CH}-CH_2CH_2-OH \ \underset{}{\overset{H^+}{\rightleftharpoons}}$$

Acetic acid (excess)   Isopentyl alcohol

$$CH_3-\overset{\overset{\displaystyle O}{\|}}{C}-O-CH_2CH_2-\overset{\overset{\displaystyle CH_3}{|}}{CH}-CH_3 \ + \ H_2O$$

Isopentyl acetate

Isopentyl acetate is prepared by the direct esterification of acetic acid with isopentyl alcohol. Because the equilibrium does not favor the formation of the ester, it must be shifted to the right, in favor of the product, by using an excess of one of the starting materials. Acetic acid is used in excess because it is less expensive than isopentyl alcohol and more easily removed from the reaction mixture.

In the isolation procedure, much of the excess acetic acid and the remaining isopentyl alcohol are removed by extraction with sodium bicarbonate and water. After drying with anhydrous sodium sulfate, the ester is purified by distillation. The purity of the liquid product is analyzed by performing a microscale boiling point determination or infrared spectroscopy.

SPECIAL INSTRUCTIONS

Be careful when dispensing sulfuric and glacial acetic acids. They are corrosive and will attack your skin if you make contact with them. If you get one of these acids on your skin, wash the affected area with copious quantities of running water for 10–15 minutes.

Because a 1-hour reflux is required, you should start the experiment at the beginning of the laboratory period. During the reflux period, you may perform other work.

SUGGESTED WASTE DISPOSAL

Any aqueous solutions should be placed in a container specially designated for dilute aqueous waste. Place any excess ester in the nonhalogenated organic waste container.

PROCEDURE

Apparatus

Using a 5-mL conical vial, assemble a reflux apparatus using a water-cooled condenser. Top the condenser with a drying tube that contains a loose plug of glass wool. The purpose of the drying tube is to control odors rather than to protect the reaction from water. Use a hot plate and an aluminum block for heating.

Preparation

Remove the empty 5-mL conical vial, weigh it, and record its weight. Place approximately 1.0 mL of isopentyl alcohol ($MW = 88.2$, $d = 0.813$ g/mL) in the vial using an automatic pipet or a dispensing pump. Reweigh the vial containing the alcohol and subtract the tare weight to obtain an accurate weight for the alcohol. Add 1.5 mL of glacial acetic acid ($MW = 60.1$, $d = 1.06$ g/mL) using an automatic pipet or dispensing pump. Using a disposable Pasteur pipet, add two to three drops of concentrated sulfuric acid. Swirl the liquid to mix. Add a small boiling stone (or a magnetic spin vane) and reattach the vial to the apparatus.

Reflux

Bring the mixture to a boil (aluminum block at about 150–160°C). Be sure to stir the mixture if you are using a spin vane instead of a boiling stone. Continue heating under reflux for 60–75 minutes. Remove the heating source and allow the mixture to cool to room temperature.

Workup

Disassemble the apparatus and, using a forceps, remove the boiling stone (or spin vane). Using a calibrated Pasteur pipet, slowly add 1.0 mL of 5% aqueous sodium bicarbonate to the cooled mixture in the conical vial. Stir the mixture in the vial with a microspatula until carbon dioxide evolution is no longer vigorous. Then cap the vial and shake *gently* with venting until the evolution of gas is complete. Using a Pasteur pipet, remove the lower aqueous layer and discard it. Repeat the extraction two more times, as outlined previously, using a fresh 1.0-mL portion of 5% sodium bicarbonate solution each time.

If droplets of water are evident in the vial containing the ester, transfer the ester to a dry conical vial using a dry Pasteur pipet. Dry the ester over granular anhydrous sodium sulfate. Allow the capped solution to stand for 10–15 minutes. Transfer the dry ester with a Pasteur pipet into a 3-mL conical vial while leaving the drying agent behind. If necessary, pick out any granules of sodium sulfate with the end of a spatula.

Distillation

Add a boiling stone (or a magnetic spin vane) to the dry ester. Clamping the glass-ware, assemble a distillation apparatus using a Hickman still and a water-cooled condenser on top of a hot plate with an aluminum heating block. In order to control odors, rather than to keep the reaction dry, top the apparatus with a drying tube packed loosely with a small amount of calcium chloride held in place by bits of cotton or glass wool. Begin the distillation by turning on the hot plate (about 180°C). Stir the mixture if you are using a spin vane instead of a boiling stove. Continue the distillation until only one or two drops of liquid remain in the distilling the distilling vial. If the Hickman head fills before the distillation is complete, it may be necessary to empty it using a Pasteur pipet and transfer the distillate to a tared (preweighed) conical vial. Unless you have a side-ported Hickman still, it will be necessary to remove the condenser in order to perform the transfer. When the distillation is complete, transfer the final portion of the distillate to this same vial.

Determination of Yield

Weigh the product and calculate the percentage yield of the ester. Determine its boiling point (bp 142°C) using a microscale boiling-point determination.

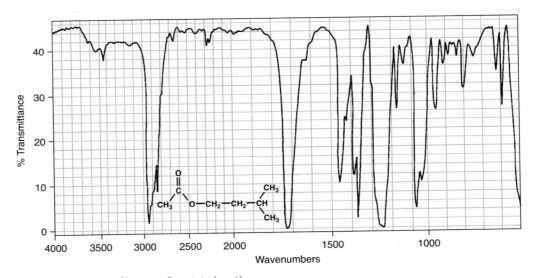

Infrared spectrum of isopentyl acetate (neat).

Infrared Spectroscopy

At your instructor's option, obtain an infrared spectrum. Compare the spectrum with the one reproduced in this experiment and include it with your report to the instructor. If any of your sample remains after performing the determination of the infrared spectrum, submit it in a properly labeled vial along with your report.

QUESTIONS

1. One method for favoring the formation of an ester is to add excess acetic acid. Suggest another method, involving the right-hand side of the equation, that will favor the formation of the ester.

2. Why is it easier to remove excess acetic acid from the products than excess isopentyl alcohol?

3. Why is the reaction mixture extracted with sodium bicarbonate? Give an equation and explain its relevance.

4. Which starting material is the limiting reagent in this procedure? Which reagent is used in excess? How great is the molar excess (how many times greater)?

5. How many grams are there in 1.00 mL of isopentyl acetate? You will need to look up the density of isopentyl acetate in a handbook.

6. How many moles of isopentyl acetate are there in 1.00 g of isopentyl acetate? You will need to calculate the molecular weight of isopentyl acetate.

7. Suppose that 1.00 mL of isopentyl alcohol was reacted with excess acetic acid and that 1.00 g of isopentyl acetate was obtained as product. Calculate the percentage yield.

8. Outline a separation scheme for isolating pure isopentyl acetate from the reaction mixture.

9. Interpret the principal absorption bands in the infrared spectrum of isopentyl acetate. (Technique 25 may be of some help in answering this question.)

10. Write a mechanism for the acid-catalyzed esterification of acetic acid with isopentyl alcohol. You may need to consult the chapter on carboxylic acids in your lecture textbook

This is an individual report worth 50 points.
Studnets turning in reports identical or similar to past or current reports will be given an automatic zero.

See the handout called "Report Outline" in the "Course Documents" section for a detailed explanation of report requirements. Figures should be computer generated (there is a link in the external link section on blackboard for free drawing software.)

DIRECTIONS for Typed Report (Be concise! Most typed reports do not need to be more than 5 pages total)
Overall quality (3 points)

Page One
 Cover Page (3 points)
 Make sure to have an acceptable title. See the outline on blackboard for more detail

Page Two
 Abstract (8 points)
 A brief summary of the experiment and the results is necessary. Make sure to write out the overall reaction with percent yield. No more than one page double spaced.

Page Three and Following
 Introduction (10 points)
 The introduction discusses everything you knew and/or expected *prior* to the reaction. It should always include an overall reaction with a verbal explanation. Once we start learning mechanisms you will also need to include that (so no need to give it for this reaction). It should also include a description of how you plan to characterize your product (i.e. how will you know if your experiment was successful?) See the handout on blackboard for more detail.
 • draw overall reaction & mechanism using a chemical drawing program
 • discuss and explain reaction & mechanism and reactive species
 • discuss expected results/goals
 • discuss how you *plan* to characterize product (i.e. boiling point and IR) - but DO NOT give the results yet

 Procedure - (6 points)
 No more than ½ page double-spaced. Be brief! Use passive past tense and NEVER use I/we.

 Results and Calculations (10 points)
 Attach and complete the table on the next page. This is your "numbers" section. So make sure to supply the literature and experimental boiling point of the product. Supply the percent yield and percent yield calculations. Attach the IRs and label the important peaks.

 Discussion and Conclusions (10 points)
 Discuss the overall experiment. The discussion should allude back to everything in the introduction as well as tie-up any unpredicted results. Be sure to discuss all sources of error and possible synthetic routes to improve the reaction and yield. A good discussion answers the questions "Did it work?", "What good was this?", "Should I change anything next time?" You should explain why it worked, or speculate (based on sound reasoning) why it didn't work. See the handout on blackboard for more detail.

Complete and attach this sheet to you report for the data section

Distillation Data

Fraction #	Distillation Temperature (°C)	Volume (mL) or Mass (mg) of fraction	Other (color, odor, etc)
1			
2			
3			
4			

Product Data

Fraction number(s) which contained product: _____

Microscale boiling point of isolated product: _____

Literature boiling point of isopentyl acetate: _____

Mass of isolated product: _____

Expected mass of isolated product: _____

Percent yield of product: _____

Percent yield calculations:

IRData – *attach and label IR and starting compound and product*

LAB H:
ADAPTED FROM EXPERIMENT #20

Reactivities of Some Alkyl Halides

S_N1/S_N2 reactions

Relative rates

Reactivities

The reactivities of alkyl halides in nucleophilic substitution reactions depend on two important factors: reaction conditions and substrate structure. The reactivities of several substrate types will be examined under both S_N1 and S_N2 reaction conditions in this experiment.

Sodium Iodide or Potassium Iodide in Acetone

A reagent composed of sodium iodide or potassium iodide dissolved in acetone is useful in classifying alkyl halides according to their reactivity in an S_N2 reaction. Iodide ion is an excellent nucleophile, and acetone is a nonpolar solvent. The tendency to form a precipitate increases the completeness of the reaction. Sodium iodide and potassium iodide are soluble in acetone, but the corresponding bromides and chlorides are not soluble. Consequently, as bromide ion or chloride ion is produced, the ion is precipitated from the solution. According to LeChâtelier's Principle, the precipitation of a product from the reaction solution drives the equilibrium toward the right; such is the case in the reaction described here:

$$R\text{---}Cl + Na^+I^- \longrightarrow RI + NaCl \text{ (s)}$$

$$R\text{---}Br + Na^+I^- \longrightarrow RI + NaBr \text{ (s)}$$

Silver Nitrate in Ethanol

A reagent composed of silver nitrate dissolved in ethanol is useful in classifying alkyl halides according to their reactivity in an S_N1 reaction. Nitrate ion is a poor nucleophile, and ethanol is a moderately powerful ionizing solvent. The silver ion, because of its ability to coordinate the leaving halide ion to form a silver halide precipitate, greatly assists the ionization of the alkyl halide. Again, a precipitate as one of the reaction products also enhances the reaction.

REQUIRED READING

Before beginning this experiment, review the chapters dealing with nucleophilic substitution in your lecture textbook.

SPECIAL INSTRUCTIONS

Some compounds used in this experiment, particularly crotyl chloride and benzyl chloride, are powerful lachrymators. **Lachrymators** cause eye irritation and the formation of tears.

CAUTION

Because some of these compounds are lachrymators, perform these tests in a hood. Be careful to dispose of the test solutions in a waste container marked for halogenated organic waste. After testing, rinse the test tubes with acetone and pour the contents into the same waste container.

SUGGESTED WASTE DISPOSAL

Dispose of all the halide wastes into the container marked for halogenated waste. Any acetone washings should also be placed in the same container.

PROCEDURE

Part A. Sodium Iodide in Acetone

The Experiment

Label a series of 8 clean and dry test tubes (10 × 75-mm test tubes may be used) from 1 to 8. In each test tube place 2 mL of a 15% NaI-in-acetone solution. Now add four drops of one of the following halides to the appropriate test tube: (1) 2-chlorobutane, (2) 2-bromobutane, (3) 1-chlorobutane, (4) 1-bromobutane, (5) 2-chloro-2-methylpropane (*t*-butyl chloride), (6) crotyl chloride $CH_3CH{=}CHCH_2Cl$ (see Special Instructions), (7) benzyl chloride (α-chlorotoluene), (8) bromobenzene. Make certain you return the dropper to the proper container to avoid cross-contaminating these halides.

Reaction at Room Temperature

After adding the halide, shake the test tube[1] well to ensure adequate mixing of the alkyl halide and the solvent. Record the times needed for any precipitate or cloudiness to form.

---

[1] Do not use your thumb or a stopper. Instead, hold the top of the test tube between the thumb and index finger of one hand and "flick" the bottom of the test tube using the index finger of your other hand.

Reaction at Elevated Temperature

After about 5 minutes, place any test tubes that do not contain a precipitate in a 50°C water bath. Be careful not to allow the temperature of the water bath to exceed 50°C, because the acetone will evaporate or boil out of the test tube. After about 1 minute of heating, cool the test tubes to room temperature and note whether a reaction has occurred. Record the results.

Observations

Generally, reactive halides give a precipitate within 3 minutes at room temperature, moderately reactive halides give a precipitate when heated, and unreactive halides do not give a precipitate, even after being heated. Ignore any color changes.

Report

Record your results in tabular form in your notebook. Explain why each compound has the reactivity you observed. Explain the reactivities in terms of structure. Compare relative reactivities for compounds of similar structure.

Part B. Silver Nitrate in Ethanol

The Experiment

Label a series of ten clean and dry test tubes from 1 to 8, as described in the previous section. Add 2 mL of a 1% ethanolic silver nitrate solution to each test tube. Now add 4 drops of the appropriate halide to each test tube, using the same numbering scheme indicated for the sodium iodide test. To avoid cross-contaminating these halides, return the dropper to the proper container.

Reaction at Room Temperature

After adding the halide, shake the test tube well to ensure adequate mixing of the alkyl halide and the solvent. After thoroughly mixing the samples, record the times needed for any precipitate or cloudiness to form. Record your results as dense precipitate, cloudiness, or no precipitate/cloudiness.

Reaction at Elevated Temperature

After about 5 minutes, place any test tubes that do not contain a precipitate or cloudiness in a hot water bath at about 100°C. After about 1 minute of heating, cool the test tubes to room temperature and note whether a reaction has occurred. Record your results as dense precipitate, cloudiness, or no precipitate/cloudiness.

Observations

Reactive halides give a precipitate (or cloudiness) within 3 minutes at room temperature, moderately reactive halides give a precipitate (or cloudiness) when heated, and unreactive halides do not give a precipitate, even after being heated. Ignore any color changes.

QUESTIONS

1. In the tests with sodium iodide in acetone and silver nitrate in ethanol, why should 2-bromobutane react faster than 2-chlorobutane?

2. Why is benzyl chloride reactive in both tests, whereas bromobenzene is unreactive?

3. When benzyl chloride is treated with sodium iodide in acetone, it reacts much faster than 1-chlorobutane, even though both compounds are primary alkyl chlorides. Explain this rate difference.

4. 2-Chlorobutane reacts much more slowly than 2-chloro-2-methylpropane in the silver nitrate test. Explain this difference in reactivity.

Name _____

Name _____

TA name _____

Lab Day and Time _____

Scoring to be completed by TA:	
Part A	___ / 15 pts
Part B:	___ / 15 pts
TOTAL	___ / 30 pts

Part A: Sodium Iodide in Acetone (S$_N$2)

Data: (2 pts)

Name of substrate	Substrate (draw cmpd)	Halide (Cl$^-$ or Br$^-$)	Substrate structure (1°, 2°, 3°, allylic, sp^2…)	Precipitate? (Yes or No)	Conditions required for ppt to form (Immediate, needed heat, time, stir,…)
1-Chlorobutane	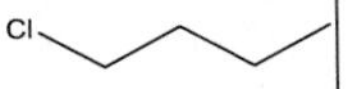 Cl⌒⌒	Cl$^-$	1°		
2-Chlorobutane			2°		
t-Butyl chloride			3°		
Crotyl chloride			Allylic 1°		
Benzyl chloride			Benzylic 1°		
1-Bromobutane					
2-Bromobutane					
Bromobenzene			sp^2		

Discussion and Conclusions: (13 pts)

1. Draw the two overall reactions (RCl &/or RBr with NaI) which occurred in part A. (2 pts)

R-Cl +

R-Br +

2. For the reactions of the alkyl halides with sodium iodide in acetone, did the type of halide affect the rate of the reaction? Hint, use your data chart to compare all structures which only vary by the type of halide (Example: 1-chlorobutane VS 1-bromobutane or 2-chlorobutane VS 2-bromobutane, etc). (2 pts)

3. Based upon your answer in #2, which substrate class as a whole was more reactive, the RCl or the RBr compounds? (2 pts)

4. For the reactions of the alkyl halides with sodium iodide in acetone, did the substrate structure affect the rate of the reaction? Hint, use your data chart to compare all structures which only vary by the type of carbon where the halide is attached (Example: 1-chlorobutane VS 2-chlorobutane VS t-butylchloride VS crotylchloride etc). (2 pt)

5. According to your answer in #4, rank the substrate structures below according to rate of reaction with sodium iodide in acetone (1 is the fastest to react and 6 is the slowest to react). If two or more compounds appear to react at the same rate, then assign them the same number (ie you may have two #1's, etc). (2 pts)

_____ Primary alky halide   _____ Allylic Primary alky halide

_____ Secondary alky halide   _____ Benzylic Primary alky halide

_____ Tertiary alky halide   _____ sp^2 alkyl halide

6. Based on your above determinations, for each pair of molecules circle the one that would react first when treated with sodium iodide in acetone and explain why. Briefly explain why. (3 pts)

A.

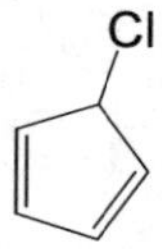

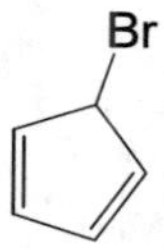

B.

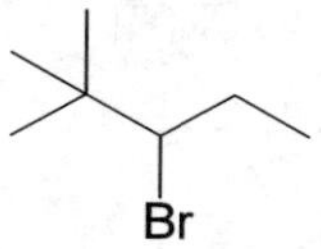

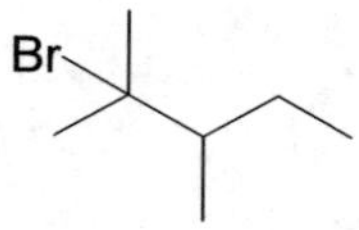

C.

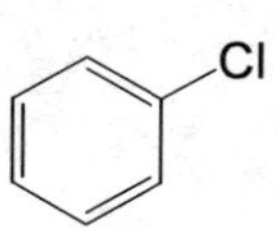

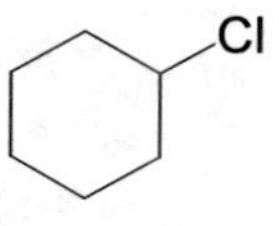

Part B: Silver Nitrate in Ethanol (S_N1)

Data: (2 pts)

Name of substrate	Substrate (draw cmpd)	Halide (Cl⁻ or Br⁻)	Substrate structure ($1°$, $2°$, $3°$, allylic, sp^2...)	Precipitate? (Yes or No)	Conditions required for ppt to form (Immediate, needed heat, time, stir,...)
1-Chlorobutane					
2-Chlorobutane					
t-Butyl chloride					
Crotyl chloride					
Benzyl chloride					
1-Bromobutane					
2-Bromobutane					
Bromobenzene					

Discussion and Conclusions: (13 pts)

7. Draw the two general reactions (RCl &/or RBr with 1% ethanolic silver nitrate) which occurred in part B. (2 pts)

    R-Cl +

    R-Br +

8. For the reactions of the alkyl halides with 1% ethanolic silver nitrate, did the type of halide affect the rate of the reaction? Hint, use your data chart to compare all structures which only vary by the type of halide (Example: 1-chlorobutane VS 1-bromobutane, and 2-chlorobutane VS 2-bromobutane, etc). (2 pts)

9. Based upon your answer in #8, which substrate class as a whole was more reactive, the RCl or the RBr compounds? (2 pts)

10. For the reactions of the alkyl halides with 1% ethanolic silver nitrate, did the substrate structure affect the rate of the reaction? Hint, use your data chart to compare all structures which only vary by the type of carbon where the halide is attached (Example: 1-chlorobutane VS 2-chlorobutane VS t-butylchloride VS crotylchloride etc). (2 pts)

11. According to your answer in #10, rank the substrate structures below according to rate of reaction with 1% ethanolic silver nitrate (1 is the fastest to react and 6 is the slowest to react). If two or more compounds appear to react at the same rate, then assign them the same number (ie you may have two #1's, etc). (2 pts)

_____ Primary alky halide   _____ Allylic Primary alky halide

_____ Secondary alky halide   _____ Benzylic Primary alky halide

_____ Tertiary alky halide   _____ sp^2 alky halide

12. Based on your above determinations, for each pair of molecules circle the one that would react first when treated with 1% ethanolic silver nitrate and explain why. Briefly explain why. (3 pts)

A.

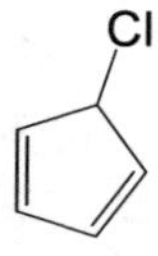

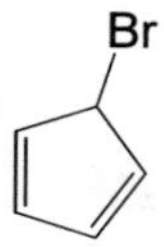

B.

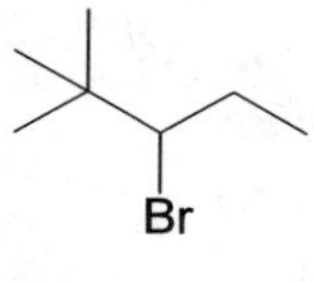

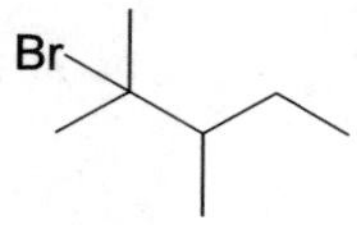

C.

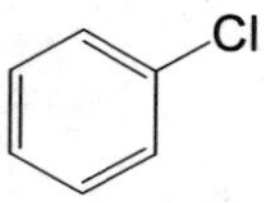

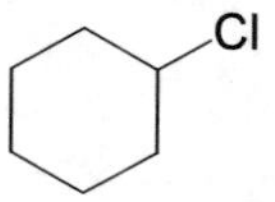

80

LAB I:
ADAPTED FROM EXPERIMENT #25

4-Methylcyclohexene

Preparation of an alkene
Dehydration of an alcohol
Distillation
Bromine and permanganate tests for unsaturation

4-Methylcyclohexanol → (H₃PO₄/H₂SO₄, Δ) → 4-Methylcyclohexene + H₂O

Alcohol dehydration is an acid-catalyzed reaction performed by strong, concentrated mineral acids such as sulfuric and phosphoric acids. The acid protonates the alcoholic hydroxyl group, permitting it to dissociate as water. Loss of a proton from the intermediate (elimination) brings about an alkene. Because sulfuric acid often causes extensive charring in this reaction, phosphoric acid, which is comparatively free of this problem, is a better choice. To make the reaction proceed faster, however, a minimal amount of sulfuric acid will also be used.

The equilibrium that attends this reaction will be shifted in favor of the product by distilling it from the reaction mixture as it is formed. The 4-methylcyclohexene (bp 101–102°C) will codistill with the water that is also formed. By continuously removing the products, one can obtain a high yield of 4-methylcyclohexene. Because the starting material, 4-methylcyclohexanol, also has a somewhat low boiling point (bp 171– 173°C), the distillation must be done carefully so that the alcohol does not also distill.

Unavoidably, a small amount of phosphoric acid codistills with the product. It is removed by washing the distillate mixture with a saturated sodium chloride solution. This step also partially removes the water from the 4-methylcyclohexene layer; the drying process will be completed by allowing the product to stand over anhydrous sodium sulfate.

Compounds containing double bonds react with a bromine solution (red) to decolorize it. Similarly, they react with a solution of potassium permanganate (purple) to discharge its color and produce a brown precipitate (MnO₂). These reactions are often used as qualitative tests to determine the presence of a double bond in an organic molecule. Both tests will be performed on the 4-methylcyclohexene formed in this experiment.

SPECIAL INSTRUCTIONS

Phosphoric and sulfuric acids are corrosive. Do not allow either acid to touch your skin.

If you must store the 4-methylcyclohexene, place it in a conical vial sealed with a glass or Teflon stopper, an O-ring, and a compression cap. Store it in a freezer. The product is extremely volatile and is easily lost. When you remove the vial from the freezer, loosen the stopper immediately or it may expand and be difficult to remove. WARNING: It is not adequate to store the sample in a conical vial with a septum liner and cap. Conical vials typically have chips on the top edge, and the septum liners, which rest on this edge, do not make an adequate seal to contain the vapors.

SUGGESTED WASTE DISPOSAL

Any organic residues should be discarded in an organic waste container designated for the disposal of *nonhalogenated* wastes. Discard the solutions that remain after the bromine test for unsaturation in an organic waste container designated for the disposal of *halogenated* wastes. The solutions that remain after the potassium permanganate test should be discarded into a waste container specifically marked for the disposal of heavy-metal wastes. Aqueous solutions should be placed in the container designated for that purpose.

4-Methylcyclohexene
(Microscale Procedure)

PROCEDURE

Apparatus Assembly

Place 1.5 mL of 4-methycyclohexanol ($MW = 114.2$) in a tared 5-mL conical vial and reweigh the vial to determine an accurate weight for the alcohol. Add 0.40 mL of 85% phosphoric acid and six drops of concentrated sulfuric acid to the vial. Mix the liquids thoroughly using a glass stirring rod and add a boiling stone or a magnetic spin vane. Assemble a distillation apparatus and use a water-cooled condenser. It is recommended that you include the drying tube, filled with calcium chloride, as an odor-control measure.

Dehydration

Start circulating the cooling water in the condenser and heat the mixture until the product begins to distill (aluminum block or sand bath set to about 160–180°C). If you use an aluminum block for heating, place aluminum collars around the conical vial. Stir the mixture if you are using a spin vane instead of a boiling stone. The heating should be regulated so that the distillation requires about 30–45 minutes, heating slowly at the beginning.

During the distillation, use a Pasteur pipet to remove the distillate from the well of the Hickman head when necessary. You must remove the condenser when performing this experiment, unless you have a Hickman head with a side port. In that case, you can remove the distillate through the side port without removing the condenser. Transfer the distillate to a clean, dry, 3-mL conical vial, which should be capped except when liquid is being added. Continue the distillation until no more liquid is being distilled. This can be best determined by observing when boiling in the conical vial has ceased. Also, the volume of liquid remaining in the vial should be about 0.5 mL when distillation is complete.

When distillation is complete, remove as much distillate as possible from the Hickman head and transfer it to the 3-mL conical vial. Then, using a Pasteur pipet with the tip slightly bent, rinse the sides of the inside wall of the Hickman head with 1.0 mL of saturated sodium chloride. Do this thoroughly so that as much liquid as possible is washed down into the well of the Hickman head. Transfer this liquid to the 3-mL conical vial.

Isolation and Drying of Product

Allow the layers to separate and remove the bottom aqueous layer. Using a dry Pasteur pipet, transfer the organic layer to a small test tube, and dry it over granular anhydrous sodium sulfate. Place a stopper in the test tube and set it aside for 10–15 minutes to remove the last traces of water. Carefully transfer as much distillate as possible to a small tared conical vial with a cap. Weigh the product ($MW = 96.2$) and calculate the percentage yield.

Boiling-Point Determination and Spectroscopy[2]

At the instructor's option, determine a more accurate boiling point on your sample using the microboiling-point method, and obtain the infared spectrum of 4-methylcyclohexene. Because 4-methylcyclohexene is so volatile, you must work quickly to obtain a good spectrum using sodium chloride plates. Compare the spectrum with the one shown in this experiment. After performing the tests below, submit your sample, along with the report, to the instructor.

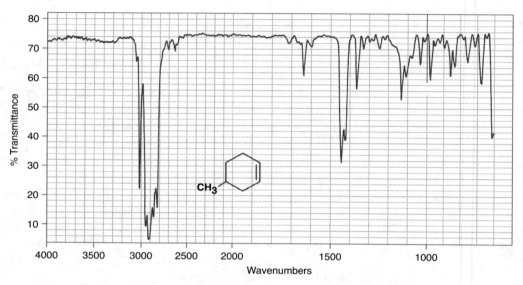

Infrared spectrum of 4-methylcyclohexene (neat).

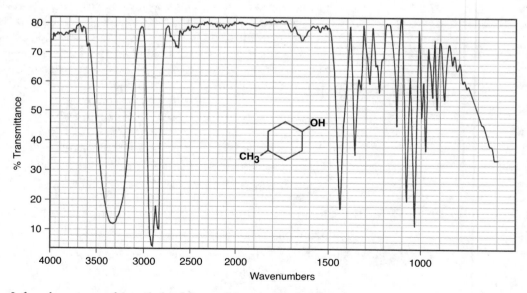

Infrared spectrum of 4-methylcyclohexanol (neat).

UNSATURATION TESTS

Place four to five drops of 4-methycyclohexanol in each of two small test tubes. In each of another pair of small test tubes, place four to five drops of the 4-methylcyclohexene you prepared. Do not confuse the test tubes. Take one test tube from each group, and add a solution of bromine in carbon tetrachloride or methylene chloride, drop by drop, to the contents of the test tube, until the red color is no longer discharged. Record the result in each case, including the number of drops required. Test the remaining two test tubes in a similar fashion with a solution of potassium permanganate. Because aqueous potassium permanganate is not miscible with organic compounds, you will have to add about 0.3 mL of 1,2-dimethoxyethane to each test tube before making the test. Record your results and explain them.

QUESTIONS

1. Outline a mechanism for the dehydration of 4-methylcyclohexanol catalyzed by phosphoric acid.

2. What major alkene product is produced by dehydrating the following alcohols?

   (a) Cyclohexanol

   (b) 1-Methylcyclohexanol

   (c) 2-Methylcyclohexanol

   (d) 2,2-Dimethylcyclohexanol

   (e) 1,2-Cyclohexanediol (*Hint:* Consider keto–enol tautomerism.)

3. Compare and interpret the infrared spectra of 4-methylcyclohexene and 4-methylcyclohexanol.

4. Identify the C-H out-of-plane bending vibrations in the infrared spectrum of 4-methylcyclohexene. What structural information can be obtained from these bands?

5. In this experiment, 1.0 mL of saturated sodium chloride is used to rinse the Hickman head after the initial distillation. Why is saturated sodium chloride, rather than pure water, used for this procedure and the subsequent washing of the organic layer?

30 points
Names: _____ & _____
TA Name: _____
Lab Day & Time: _____

1. In lab you synthesized 4-methylcyclohexene from 4-methylcyclohexanol.

    a. Draw the mechanism for the synthesis of 4-methylcyclohexene from 4-methylcyclohexanol.
        Make sure to include all steps and curved arrows for all electron movements. (5 pts)

    b. Before the elimination mechanism began, the first step is a protonation. Clearly explain WHY this
        needs to occur. In other words, why would the elimination not occur without this step first? Hint:
        think leaving group ability. (2 pt)

2. This reaction requires heat to overcome the activation energy. However, instead of a standard reflux apparatus you set-up a distillation apparatus. What was the purpose of this set-up and why did it help the reaction proceed faster? (4 pts)

3. To support that you made the correct product, you compared the boiling point of your product to the literature value. What were those boiling points? (3 pts)
   a. literature boiling point for 4-methylcyclohexene _____
   b. synthesized and purified 4-methylcyclohexene product _____
   c. Does this support that you made 4-methylcyclohexene?

4. To further support that you made your product you performed unsaturation tests.
   a. Provide the organic products and the colors of all the compounds (4 pts)

Bromine test

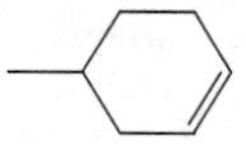

+ Br_2 → $\dfrac{CH_2Cl_2 \text{ or}}{CCl_4 \text{ solvent}}$

color: _____   color: _____   color: _____

Permanganate test

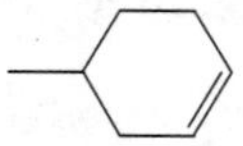

+ $KMnO_4$ → $\dfrac{1,2\text{-dimethoxyethane}}{\text{\&/or other solvents}}$ + MnO_2

color: _____   color: _____   color: _____   color: <u>brown</u>

   b. Explain why these two tests support the presence (or absence) of a double bond in your product. (2 pts)

5. The third way you supported that you made 4-methylcyclohexene was by taking the IR of the product and comparing it to the 4-methylcyclohexanol starting material.
   a. Attach the IR for the both 4-methylcyclohexanol and 4-methylcyclohexene. Draw the structure on the IR and then match all the important non-fingerprint region peaks with the correct bonds in the structure. (3 pts)

   b. Explain how you are able to use the IRs to support if you did or did not make the desired 4-methylcyclohexene product. (3 pts)

6. Draw the major alkene product(s) for each reaction below. Hint: think of the mechanism and *possible* rearrangements... (4 pts)

a. H_3PO_4/H_2SO_4 / H_2O heat →

b. H_3PO_4/H_2SO_4 / H_2O heat →

c. H_3PO_4/H_2SO_4 / H_2O heat →

d. H_3PO_4/H_2SO_4 / H_2O heat →
makes two major products